LABORATORY EXPERIMENTS

CHARLES H. CORWIN

For *Basic Chemistry*
G. William Daub • William S. Seese

Custom Edition for
California State University, San Bernadino

Taken from:

Laboratory Experiments by Charles H. Corwin

for *Basic Chemistry,* Seventh Edition
by G. William Daub, William S. Seese

PEARSON
Custom
Publishing

PEARSON
Prentice
Hall

Taken from:

Laboratory Experiments by Charles H. Corwin for
Basic Chemistry, Seventh Edition
by G. William Daub, William S. Seese
Copyright © 1996 by Prentice-Hall, Inc.
A Pearson Education Company
Upper Saddle River, New Jersey 07458

This special edition published in cooperation with Pearson Custom Publishing.

Printed in the United States of America

10 9 8 7 6 5 4 3 2 1

ISBN 0-536-12290-3

2005180186

BK

Please visit our web site at *www.pearsoncustom.com*

PEARSON CUSTOM PUBLISHING
75 Arlington Street, Suite 300, Boston, MA 02116
A Pearson Education Company

Contents

*Assigned Student Unknowns.

Safety Precautions

The laboratory can be but is not necessarily a dangerous place. With intelligent precautions and a proper understanding of techniques, the laboratory is no more dangerous than any other classroom. Most of the precautions are just common sense practices.

1. Wear safety glasses or goggles at all times while working in the laboratory.
2. Wear shoes at all times.
3. Eating, drinking, and smoking are prohibited in the laboratory at all times.
4. Know where to find and how to use the first-aid equipment and fire extinguisher.
5. Consider all chemicals to be hazardous unless instructed otherwise.
6. If chemicals come into contact with your skin or eyes, wash immediately with large amounts of water and then consult your laboratory instructor.
7. Never directly smell any vapor or gas. Instead waft a small sample toward your nose.

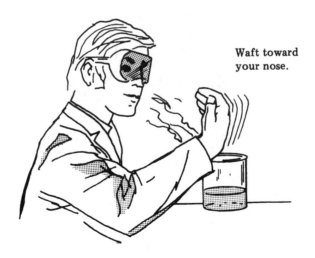

Waft toward your nose.

8. Any reactions involving dangerous chemicals or unpleasant odors are to be performed in the hood.

9. Never point a test tube which you are heating at yourself or your neighbor—it may erupt like a geyser.

10. Always pour acids into water, not water into acid, because the heat of solution will cause the water to boil and the acid to splatter.

11. When inserting glass tubing or thermometers into stoppers, *lubricate the tubing and the hole in the stopper with glycerol or water.* Wrap the glass in a towel and grasp the tubing as close to the end being inserted as possible. Slide the glass into the rubber stopper with a twisting motion. Keep your hands as close together as possible in order to eliminate the possibility of breakage.

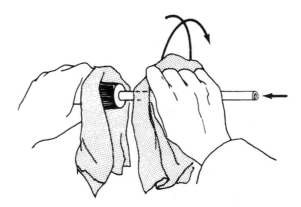

12. Clean up all broken glassware *immediately*.

13. Many common reagents, for example, alcohols, acetone, and especially ether, are highly flammable. *Do not use them anywhere near open flames.*

14. No unauthorized experiments are to be performed.

15. Observe all special precautions mentioned in the Prelaboratory Assignment of each experiment.

16. NOTIFY THE INSTRUCTOR IMMEDIATELY IN CASE OF AN ACCIDENT.

COMMON LABORATORY EQUIPMENT

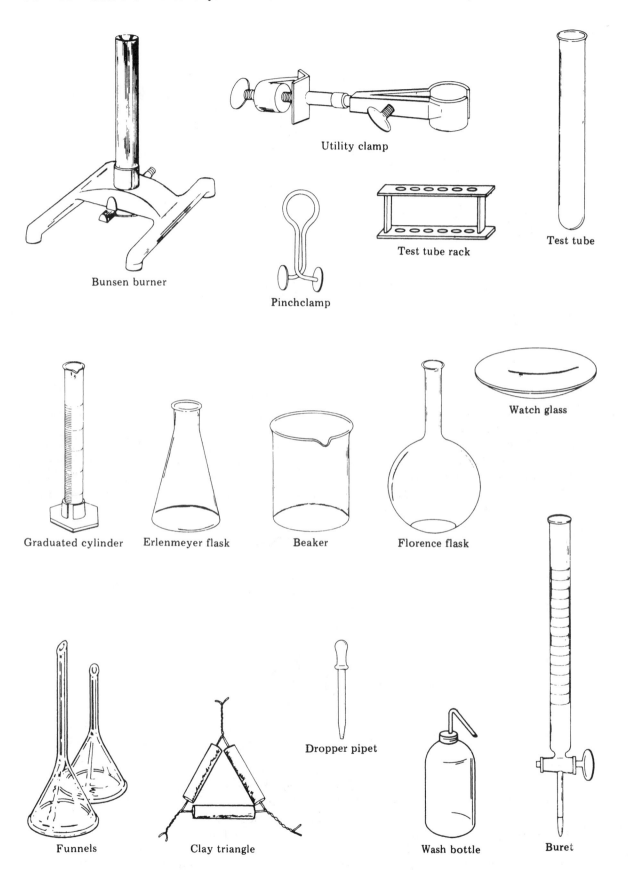

Utility clamp

Test tube

Test tube rack

Bunsen burner

Pinchclamp

Graduated cylinder   Erlenmeyer flask   Beaker   Florence flask

Watch glass

Funnels   Clay triangle   Dropper pipet   Wash bottle   Buret

3

COMMON LABORATORY EQUIPMENT

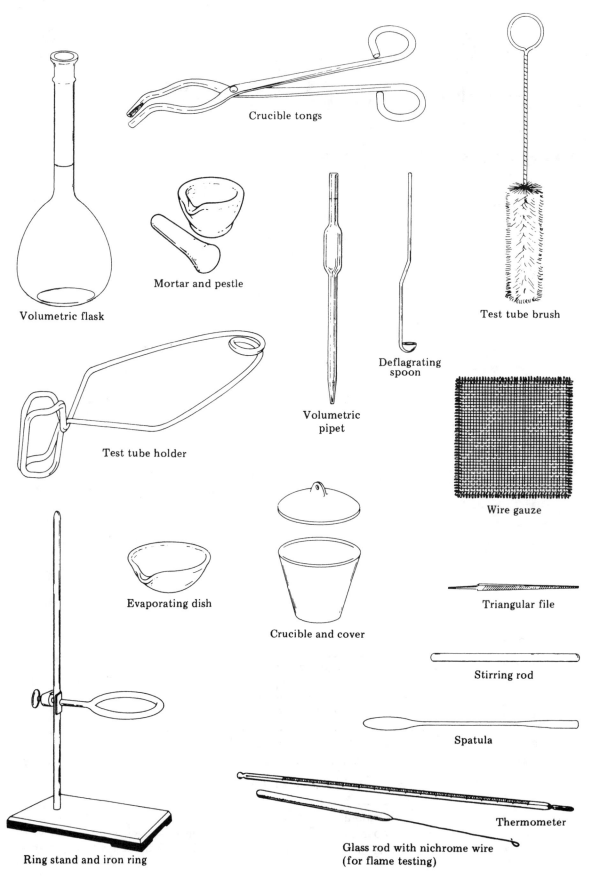

Crucible tongs

Mortar and pestle

Volumetric flask

Test tube brush

Deflagrating spoon

Volumetric pipet

Wire gauze

Test tube holder

Evaporating dish

Triangular file

Crucible and cover

Stirring rod

Spatula

Ring stand and iron ring

Thermometer

Glass rod with nichrome wire
(for flame testing)

Scientific Observations

1. To gain experience in recording and explaining experimental observations.
2. To develop skill in handling glassware and transferring solid and liquid chemicals.
3. To become familiar with safety precautions in the laboratory.

DISCUSSION

Chemistry is the branch of science that studies matter and the changes that matter undergoes. Science can be defined simply as organized knowledge. Scientific knowledge is gathered systematically by performing thoughtful experiments, carefully recording observations, and ultimately drawing some conclusions. This procedure is known as the scientific method and involves three steps (Figure 1-1).

1. Experimentation – collecting data by observation of chemical changes under controlled conditions.
2. Hypothesizing – formulating a tentative proposal to correlate and explain the experimental data.
3. Theorizing – stating a formal theory or scientific law after extensive testing of the hypothesis.

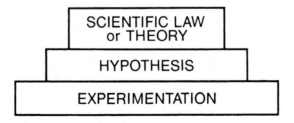

FIGURE 1-1   The scientific method.

Hypotheses are frequently proven invalid although not always immediately. Historically, chemists and physicists have been slow to abandon an acceptable theory in order to adopt a new one. Scientists exercise caution in drawing conclusions, knowing that nature reveals itself in glimpses

5

and at times appears contradictory. Hypotheses may be discarded, modified, or on rare occasions, after rigorous testing, be elevated to the status of a scientific law or theory.

PROBLEM EXAMPLE 1-1

Mercury oxide, an orange powder, is placed in a test tube and heated for two minutes. A wooden splint is ignited and extinguished. The glowing splint is then inserted into the test tube.

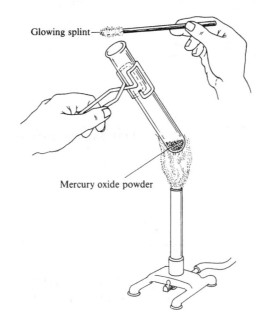

Glowing splint

Mercury oxide powder

FIGURE 1-2 Heating a compound in a test tube and testing for an evolved gas.

Observation	Hypothesis
• A silver metal forms on the inside of the test tube. • The glowing splint bursts into flames.	• Mercury and oxygen are produced from heating mercury oxide.

EQUIPMENT AND CHEMICALS

A. Instructor Demonstrations

Equipment

- 1000 mL Florence flask with stopper
- large Erlenmeyer flask with stopper
- stir rod
- 150 mL beaker
- matches
- fire extinguisher
- mortar and pestle
- wash bottle
- evaporating dish

Chemicals

- disappearing blue solution (10 g glucose in 300 mL 0.5 M KOH + 10 mL of 0.1 g/L methylene blue solution)
- copper, Cu metal
- concentrated nitric acid, 16 M HNO_3
- sugar, powdered $C_{12}H_{22}O_{11}$
- concentrated sulfuric acid, 18 M H_2SO_4
- ethanol, C_2H_5OH
- ammonium nitrate, solid NH_4NO_3
- zinc, Zn powder

B. Student Experiments

- 16 × 150 mm test tubes (2)
- scoopula
- 250 mL beaker
- graduated cylinder
- ball-and-stick models

- ammonium chloride, solid NH_4Cl
- calcium chloride, solid $CaCl_2$
- iron metal (e.g., a nail)
- calcium, Ca metal
- copper (II) sulfate solution, 0.1 M $CuSO_4$
- mercury (II) nitrate solution, 0.1 M $Hg(NO_3)_2$
- potassium iodide solution, 0.1 M KI

PROCEDURE

A. Instructor Demonstrations. The following experiments are intended to provide interesting chemical demonstrations. The instructor while performing the demonstrations may wish to discuss laboratory safety.

You will record your observations in the Data Table and then propose a hypothesis to explain the observed event.

1. *Disappearing Blue.* Observe the clear solution in the stoppered 1000 mL Florence flask. Lift the flask and shake it once with your thumb firmly on the stopper. Repeat the procedure a couple of times.
2. *Copper Smog.* Place a piece of copper metal (for example, a penny) in a large Erlenmeyer flask. Pour concentrated nitric acid into the flask so as to cover the metal and stopper tightly.

   NOTE: After the metal has stopped reacting, the instructor may wish to empty the flask contents into a beaker of water.

3. *Black Foam.* Half fill a 150 mL beaker with powdered sugar. Add 15 mL of concentrated sulfuric acid and stir slowly with a glass rod.
4. *Cold Heat.* Add 40 mL of ethanol to 60 mL of water in a 150 mL beaker. Solicit a clean handkerchief from a student and soak it in the alcohol solution. Squeeze the excess solution out of the handkerchief, spread it on a lab bench, and ignite it.

   NOTE: The effect is better with the lights dimmed. The instructor may wish to use the fire extinguisher and discuss the flammability of alcohol.

5. *Water Hazard.* Grind about 3 g of ammonium nitrate in a mortar with a pestle. Empty the powder into an evaporating dish. Liberally sprinkle fresh zinc dust over the mixture. Stand back and play a stream of distilled water from a wash bottle onto the chemicals.

   NOTE: The reaction is quite exothermic and should be performed with *caution*. A few crystals of iodine enhance the effect.

B. Student Experiments. Record your observations for each of the following in the Data Table. Propose hypotheses to explain your observations.

1. *Hot and Cold.* Add a scoopula of ammonium chloride to one test tube and calcium chloride to the other. Half fill each test tube with distilled water. Place your hand around the bottom of each test tube.

   NOTE: Empty chemicals into the sink followed by water.

2. *Active and Unreactive.* Half fill a 250 mL beaker with distilled water. Place an iron nail and a piece of calcium metal in the water. Record your observations and make a hypothesis.

3. *Copper Nails.* Half fill a 250 mL beaker with copper(II) sulfate solution. Place an iron nail in the solution. Wait a few minutes then record your observations.

4. *Here and Gone.* Measure about 10 mL of mercury(II) nitrate into a graduated cylinder. Add 20 mL of potassium iodide solution into the graduated cylinder. Record your observations.

    Add an additional 30 mL of potassium iodide into the graduated cylinder and mix the contents. Record your observations and formulate an hypothesis.

5. *Mirror Images.* Given a ball-and-stick model kit, construct the model shown in Figure 1-3. The abbreviations below are as follows: B—black, Y—yellow, O—orange, R—red, and G—green.

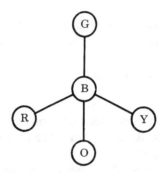

FIGURE 1-3 Ball-and-stick model.

Using additional balls and sticks, construct a second model identical to the first. Notice the two models are superimposable.

On one of the models, exchange the positions of the red and yellow after disconnecting the balls from the sticks. Are the two models now superimposable? Diagram each model in the Data Table.

PRELABORATORY ASSIGNMENT*

1. In your own words define the following terms: chemistry, experimentation, hypothesis, science, scientific law, scientific method, theory.

2. Identify the following: Erlenmeyer flask, beaker, wash bottle, Florence flask, test tube, graduated cylinder, mortar and pestle. See Common Laboratory Equipment, pages 4 and 5.

3. Where are directions given for transferring a solid or a liquid from a reagent bottle?

4. Which of the following chemicals should be handled knowledgeably and carefully: concentrated acids, alcohol, ammonium nitrate, calcium chloride, organic chemicals, distilled water?

5. What should you do if any chemical comes in contact with your skin?

*Answers in Appendix II.

NAME _____

SECTION _____

DATA TABLE FOR SCIENTIFIC OBSERVATIONS

A. Instructor Demonstrations

    1. Disappearing Blue

        Observation   *Hypothesis*

    2. Copper Smog

        Observation   *Hypothesis*

    3. Black Foam

        Observation   *Hypothesis*

    4. Cold Heat

        Observation   *Hypothesis*

    5. Water Hazard

        Observation   *Hypothesis*

B. Student Experiments

    1. Hot and Cold

           Observation   *Hypothesis*

    2. Active and Unreactive

           Observation   *Hypothesis*

    3. Copper Nails

           Observation   *Hypothesis*

    4. Here and Gone

           Observation   *Hypothesis*

    5. Mirror Images

           Observation   *Hypothesis*

1. The principles of chemistry have been developed by using the scientific method. State and describe the three steps of this procedure.

   (a)

   (b)

   (c)

2. Indicate in the space provided whether each of the following laboratory safety precautions are *true* or *false*.

   (a) _____ Wear safety glasses or goggles at all times while working in the laboratory.

   (b) _____ Wear shoes at all times.

   (c) _____ Eating, drinking, and smoking are strictly prohibited in the laboratory at all times.

   (d) _____ Know where to find and how to use safety and first-aid equipment.

   (e) _____ Consider all chemicals to be hazardous unless instructed otherwise.

   (f) _____ If chemicals come into contact with your skin or eyes, wash immediately with copious amounts of water and then consult your laboratory instructor.

   (g) _____ Never taste anything. Never directly smell the source of any vapor or gas; instead, by means of your cupped hand, bring a small sample to your nose.

   (h) _____ Any reactions involving skin-irritating or dangerous chemicals, or unpleasant odors, are to be performed in the hood.

   (i) _____ When heating a chemical in a test tube, never point the open end toward yourself or your neighbor.

   (j) _____ No unauthorized experiments are to be performed.

   (k) _____ Clean up all broken glassware immediately.

   (l) _____ Always pour acids into water, not water into acid, because the heat of solution will cause the water to boil and the acid to splatter.

   (m) _____ When inserting glass tubing or thermometers into stoppers, lubricate the tubing and the hole in the stopper with glycerol or water.

   (n) _____ Do not use alcohol, acetone, or ether near open flames.

   (o) _____ Observe all special precautions mentioned in each experiment.

   (p) _____ Notify the instructor immediately in case of an accident.

3.   State whether the following instructions for working in the laboratory are *true* or *false*.

(a) _____ Read the experiment before coming to the laboratory: the Objectives, Discussion, Equipment and Chemicals, and Procedure. Do the Prelaboratory Assignment and check your answers in Appendix II.

(b) _____ Work independently unless instructed otherwise.

(c) _____ Record your observations directly in your Data Table or notebook. Do not record data on scratch paper.

(d) _____ Be aware of safety precautions and avoid accidents.

(e) _____ Pour excess liquid reagents into the sink and wash away with water.

(f) _____ Place excess solid reagents in the crock or other waste container.

(g) _____ Dispose of organic chemicals in the special waste container provided by the instructor.

(h) _____ When the experiment calls for water, use distilled water. When cleaning glassware, use tap water and then rinse with distilled water.

(i) _____ Never place chemicals directly on the balance pan.

(j) _____ Never place a hot or warm object on the balance pan. Allow the object to cool to room temperature before weighing.

(k) _____ After heating an object, do not place it on the desk top. Allow it to cool or place it on a wire gauze.

(l) _____ Clean your laboratory station upon completion of the experiment.

4.   (optional) You are given nine pennies and a platform balance.

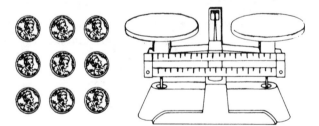

One penny is lighter than the other eight of equal mass. How can you determine the light penny in only two weighings?

Density of Liquids and Solids

OBJECTIVES

1. To determine the density of the following: water, unknown liquid, rubber stopper, unknown rectangular solid.
2. To calculate the thickness of aluminum foil given its density and the measurements of mass, length, and width.
3. To gain proficiency in performing the following experimental procedures: pipetting a liquid, weighing by difference, and determining volume by displacement.

DISCUSSION

Density is a physical property of matter that is defined as the amount of mass per unit volume; in equation form we have

$$\text{density (d)} = \frac{\text{mass (m)}}{\text{volume (V)}}$$

To determine experimentally the density of a liquid or solid, we first measure the mass using a balance. The volume can be obtained using calibrated glassware or by calculation. After collecting the data, the density is calculated from the ratio of mass to volume. In addition, the proper units must be attached to the calculated value. The density of liquids and solids is usually expressed in grams per milliliter (g/mL) or grams per cubic centimer (g/cm^3). Since by definition 1 mL = 1 cm^3, the numerical value for the density of a liquid or solid is identical in units of g/mL or g/cm^3.

To determine the mass of a liquid we will use an indirect technique called *weighing by difference* (Figure 3-1). First, we will weigh a flask empty. Next we will pipet a given volume of liquid into the flask and reweigh. The mass of the liquid is found by subtraction.

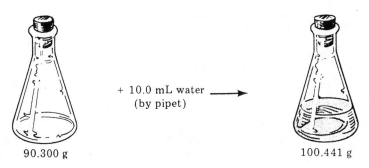

FIGURE 3-1 Weighing by difference;
100.441 − 90.300 = 10.141 g of water.

PROBLEM EXAMPLE 3-1

A 10.0 mL sample of water is pipetted into a flask. The mass of water is found from weighing by difference (see Figure 3-1). If the mass is 10.141 g, calculate the density of water.

Solution: Dividing mass by volume,

$$\frac{10.141 \text{ g}}{10.0 \text{ mL}} = 1.01 \text{ g/mL}$$

The answer is limited to three significant digits by the value in the denominator. The calculated value, 1.01 g/mL, agrees well with the theoretical value, 1.00 g/mL. The slight discrepancy is due to experimental error.

The volume of an irregular object cannot be found directly. However, its volume can be found indirectly from the amount of water it displaces. This technique is called *volume by displacement*. For example, the volume of a rubber stopper can be determined as shown in Figure 3-2. The initial reading of water in the graduated cylinder is recorded. The stopper is introduced into the cylinder and then the final reading is taken. The difference between the initial and final readings corresponds to the volume of water displaced. The volume of water displaced is equal to the volume of the rubber stopper.

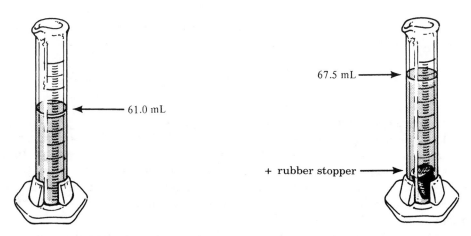

FIGURE 3-2 Volume by displacement for a rubber stopper;
67.5 − 61.0 = 6.5 mL.

PROBLEM EXAMPLE 3-2

A rubber stopper weighing 8.453 g displaces 6.5 mL of water in a graduated cylinder (Figure 3-2). What is the density of the stopper?

Solution: Dividing mass by volume,

$$\frac{8.453 \text{ g}}{6.5 \text{ mL}} = 1.3 \text{ g/mL}$$

In this example the volume has only two digits. Thus, the density is limited to two significant digits.

The volume of a solid object with regular dimensions can be found by calculation. For example, the volume of a rectangular solid is equal to its length times width times thickness.

PROBLEM EXAMPLE 3-3

The mass of a rectangular solid stainless steel block is 139.443 g. If the block measures 5.00 cm by 2.55 cm by 1.25 cm, what is the density of the stainless steel?

Solution: First, we calculate the volume of the block:

$$5.00 \text{ cm} \times 2.55 \text{ cm} \times 1.25 \text{ cm} = 15.9 \text{ cm}^3$$

Second, we find the density of the stainless steel:

$$\frac{139.443 \text{ g}}{15.9 \text{ cm}^3} = 8.77 \text{ g/cm}^3$$

The thickness of a sheet of metal foil is too thin to measure with a ruler. However, we can find the thickness indirectly by calculation. Given the mass, length, and width of a metal foil, we can use the density of the metal to calculate the thickness of the foil.

PROBLEM EXAMPLE 3-4

A rectangular sheet of tin foil has a mass of 0.571 g and measures 5.10 cm by 10.25 cm. Given the density of tin, 7.28 g/cm^3, calculate the thickness of the foil.

Solution: To calculate the thickness of the foil we must first find the volume of the foil. The volume can be calculated from the density of tin as follows:

$$0.571 \text{ g} \times \frac{1 \text{ cm}^3}{7.28 \text{ g}} = 0.0784 \text{ cm}^3$$

The thickness of the rectangular sheet of foil is found from dividing the volume by its length and width:

$$\frac{0.0784 \text{ cm}^3}{5.10 \text{ cm} \times 10.25 \text{ cm}} = 0.00150 \text{ cm} \ (1.50 \times 10^{-3} \text{ cm})$$

EQUIPMENT AND CHEMICALS

A. Instructor Demonstration

- tall glass cylinder
- methylene chloride
- hexane

- glass object
- *hard* plastic object
- ice
- cork

B–F. Student Experiments

- 125 mL Erlenmeyer flask
- 150 mL beaker
- 10 mL pipet
- pipet bulb
- unknown liquids

- 100 mL beaker
- 100 mL graduated cylinder
- #2 rubber stopper
- unknown rectangular solid
- aluminum foil, ~5 × 10 cm rectangle

PROCEDURE

A. Density Observations — Instructor Demonstration

1. Half fill a tall glass cylinder with water. Add methylene chloride until two layers are observed. Add hexane until three layers are observed. Record the positions of each layer in the Data Table.
2. Drop a glass object into the cylinder and record the observation.
3. Drop a plastic object into the cylinder; record the observation.
4. Drop a piece of ice into the cylinder; record your observation.
5. Drop a cork into the cylinder; record your observation.

B. Density of Water

1. Weigh a 125 mL Erlenmeyer flask fitted with a rubber stopper.
2. Half fill a 150 mL beaker with distilled water and pipet 10.0 mL into the flask (see Appendix VIII).
3. Reweigh the flask and stopper and determine the mass of water by difference.
4. Repeat a second trial.

   NOTE: It is not necessary to dry the flask between trials because the 10.0 mL sample of water is weighed by difference.

5. Calculate the density of the water for each trial and report the average value for both trials.

C. Density of an Unknown Liquid

1. Obtain about 25 mL of an unknown liquid in a 100 mL beaker. Record the unknown number in the Data Table.
2. Weigh a 125 mL Erlenmeyer flask fitted with a rubber stopper.
3. Condition the pipet and transfer 10.0 mL of unknown liquid into the flask.
4. Reweigh the flask and stopper and determine the mass of liquid by difference.
5. Repeat a second trial.
6. Calculate the density of the liquid for each trial and report the average value for both trials.

D. Density of a Rubber Stopper

1. Weigh a dry #2 rubber stopper.
2. Fill a 100 mL graduated cylinder about half full with water. Record the water level by observing the bottom of the meniscus and estimating to ±0.5 mL.
3. Tilt the graduated cylinder and let the stopper slowly slide into the water. Record the new level and calculate the volume by displacement for the stopper.
4. Repeat a second trial.
5. Calculate the density of the rubber stopper for each trial and report the average value for both trials.

16

E. Density of an Unknown Rectangular Solid

  1. Obtain an unknown rectangular solid and record the unknown number in the Data
      Table.
  2. Weigh the unknown solid and record the mass.
  3. Measure the length, width, and thickness with a metric ruler (see page 34). Record
      the data and find the volume of the rectangular solid.
  4. Calculate the volume of the unknown rectangular solid.

F. Thickness of Aluminum Foil

  1. Obtain a rectangular piece of aluminum foil.
  2. Record the length and width of the foil (see page 34) in the Data Table.
  3. Fold the foil twice. Weigh and record its mass.
  4. Calculate the volume and thickness of the aluminum foil. (The density of aluminum
      is 2.70 g/cm^3.)

PRELABORATORY ASSIGNMENT*

  1. In your own words, define the following terms: conditioning, density, meniscus,
      volume by displacement, weighing by difference.
  2. Record the measurement indicated by each of the following instruments. The reading
      should be consistent with the uncertainty of the instrument:
      (a) graduated cylinder

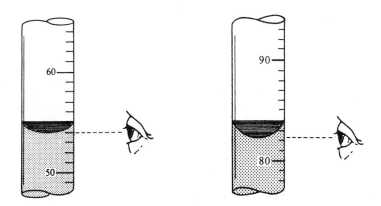

*Answers in Appendix II.

(b)   metric ruler

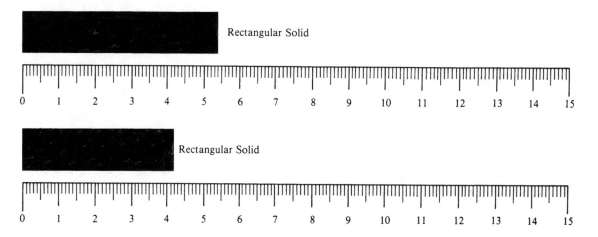

3. A 10.0 mL sample of acetone is pipetted into a stoppered flask. The mass is found by difference to be 7.899 g. Calculate the density of the liquid.
4. A piece of chalk weighing 15.60 g displaces 6.5 mL of water in a graduated cylinder. Calculate the density of the chalk.
5. A rectangular block of jade has a mass of 146.25 g and measures 10.00 cm by 3.00 cm by 1.50 cm. What is the density of the jade?
6. Find the thickness of a piece of gold foil that has a mass of 1.000 g and measures 5.00 cm by 10.00 cm. The density of gold is 18.9 g/cm^3.
7. What safety precautions must be observed in this experiment?

NAME _____

DATE _____

SECTION _____

DATA TABLE FOR DENSITY OF LIQUIDS AND SOLIDS

    A.   **Density Observations — Instructor Demonstration**   *Observation*

        methylene chloride added to water

        hexane added to water

        glass object added into cylinder

        plastic object added into cylinder

        ice added into cylinder

        cork added into cylinder

      Diagram of the Graduated Cylinder:

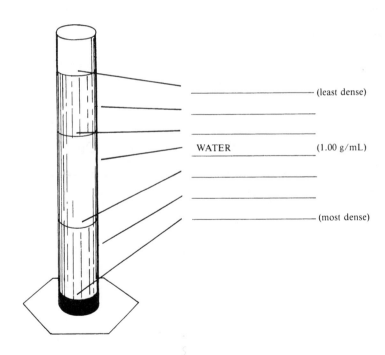

                                  _____ (least dense)

                                  _____

        WATER   _____ (1.00 g/mL)

                                  _____

                                  _____ (most dense)

B. **Density of Water**

mass of flask and stopper + water   _____g   _____g

mass of flask and stopper   _____g   _____g

mass of water   _____g   _____g

volume of water   _____mL   _____mL

Show the calculation for the density of water for trial 1.

Density of water   _____g/mL   _____g/mL

    Average density of water   _____g/mL

C. **Density of an Unknown Liquid**   **UNKNOWN #** _____

mass of flask and stopper + liquid   _____g   _____g

mass of flask and stopper   _____g   _____g

mass of unknown liquid   _____g   _____g

volume of unknown liquid   _____mL   _____mL

Show the calculation for the density of the unknown liquid for trial 1.

Density of unknown liquid   _____g/mL   _____g/mL

    Average density of unknown liquid   _____g/mL

D. **Density of a Rubber Stopper**

mass of rubber stopper	_____g	_____g
final cylinder reading	_____mL	_____mL
initial cylinder reading	_____mL	_____mL
volume of rubber stopper	_____mL	_____mL

Show the calculation of density for the rubber stopper.

Density of rubber stopper	_____g/mL	_____g/mL
Average density of rubber stopper	_____g/mL	

E. **Density of an Unknown Rectangular Solid**   UNKNOWN # _____

mass of solid	_____g	_____g
length of solid	_____cm	_____cm
width of solid	_____cm	_____cm
thickness of solid	_____cm	_____cm

Show the calculation for the volume of the rectangular solid.

Volume of solid	_____ cm^3	_____ cm^3

Show the calculation for the density of the rectangular solid.

Density of rectangular solid	_____g/cm^3	_____g/cm^3
Average density of the solid	_____g/cm^3	

F. Thickness of Aluminum Foil

length of foil   _____ cm

width of foil   _____ cm

mass of foil   _____ g

Show the calculation for the volume of the aluminum foil. (The density of aluminum is 2.70 g/cm^3.)

Volume of foil   _____ cm^3

Show the calculation for the thickness of the foil.

Thickness of foil   _____ cm

POSTLABORATORY ASSIGNMENT   NAME _____

1.   Ether floats on water and mercury sinks, as shown in the diagram below.

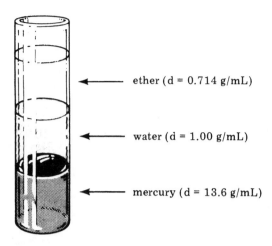

ether (d = 0.714 g/mL)

water (d = 1.00 g/mL)

mercury (d = 13.6 g/mL)

Draw in the above diagram where the following would come to rest after being **dropped into** the graduated cylinder:

(a)   a diamond (d = 3.5 g/cm^3)

(b)   a platinum bead (d = 21.4 g/cm^3)

(c)   an oak ball (d = 0.65 g/cm^3)

(d)   a piece of wax (d = 0.90 g/cm^3)

2.   A flask with stopper has a mass of 79.310 g. A 25.0 mL sample of an unknown organic liquid was pipetted into the flask and gave a total mass of 97.010 g. Find the density of the unknown liquid.

_____

3.   A sapphire gemstone has a mass of 5.600 g. Placed in a graduated cylinder, the volume increases from 47.5 mL to 49.1 mL. What is the density of the gem?

_____

4. A rectangular sheet of lead shielding is placed over the chest of a patient in a dental office while X-rays are taken. The sheet measures 95.0 cm by 45.0 cm by 0.15 cm. If the density of lead is 11.3 g/cm^3, what is the mass of the lead apron?

_____

5. Find the thickness of a sheet of titanium that measures 75.0 cm by 50.0 cm and has a mass of 2.531 kg. The density of titanium metal is 4.50 g/cm^3.

_____

6. Calculate the density of a marble that has a mass of 3.050 g and a radius of 0.63 cm. (The volume of a sphere equals $4\pi r^3/3$; where π is 3.14, and r is the radius.)

_____

7. (optional) The mass of the earth is 5.98×10^{24} kg and the diameter is 12,700 km. Assuming the earth is spherical, what is the average density of our planet in g/cm^3?

_____

3

Periodic Classification of the Elements

OBJECTIVES

1. To study the similarity of properties for groups of elements in the Periodic Table.
2. To observe the flame tests and solution reactions of some alkali and alkaline earth elements.
3. To become familiar with the reactions of chlorine water and the halides.
4. To analyze an unknown solution containing an alkali or alkaline earth element and a halide.

DISCUSSION

It was not until the beginning of the nineteenth century that the clear distinction between elements and compounds was made. At that time, the study of the composition of substance was flourishing. Chemists were discovering a vast body of knowledge about the physical and chemical properties of elements and compounds. As a result of this rapid accumulation of data, several systematic methods of classification for the elements were attempted. In 1869, the Russian chemist Dmitri Mendeleev suggested the systematic arrangement of elements according to increasing atomic mass. Mendeleev had the brilliant foresight to predict yet undiscovered elements and he represented these elements by spaces in his proposed Periodic Table of elements. The construction of the table and the ordering of elements into groups and periods was based upon observed physical and chemical properties. Mendeleev was not only able to predict the existence of six unknown elements, but also many properties of these elements.

In 1913 Harry Moseley, a 25-year-old English physicist, was working in the laboratory of Ernest Rutherford at the University of Manchester. Moseley examined X-ray emission spectra and concluded that the elements should actually be arranged in order of increasing atomic number rather than atomic mass. With few exceptions, an increase in atomic number is paralleled by an increase in atomic mass. However, the concept of increasing atomic number much more clearly explains periodic properties. The periodic recurrence of similar physical and chemical properties, based upon atomic number, is referred to as the *Periodic Law*.

The elements in the Periodic Table (Figure 7-1) are arranged in a sequence of columns and rows. The elements in vertical columns are called groups or families and possess similar chemical properties. The horizontal rows are termed periods or series. There is a general trend in physical properties for elements within a group. For example, density usually increases from the top to bottom of a group. Elements that belong to the same family also give similar chemical reactions.

GROUPS

PERIODS	1 IA	2 IIA	3 IIIB	4 IVB	5 VB	6 VIB	7 VIIB	8	9 VIII	10	11 IB	12 IIB	13 IIIA	14 IVA	15 VA	16 VIA	17 VIIA	18 VIIIA
1	1.008 H 1																	4.003 He 2
2	6.941 Li 3	9.012 Be 4											10.81 B 5	12.011 C 6	14.007 N 7	15.999 O 8	18.998 F 9	20.179 Ne 10
3	22.990 Na 11	24.305 Mg 12				TRANSITION ELEMENTS							26.982 Al 13	28.0855 Si 14	30.9738 P 15	32.06 S 16	35.453 Cl 17	39.948 Ar 18
4	39.0983 K 19	40.08 Ca 20	44.956 Sc 21	47.90 Ti 22	50.9415 V 23	51.996 Cr 24	54.938 Mn 25	55.847 Fe 26	58.933 Co 27	58.71 Ni 28	63.546 Cu 29	65.37 Zn 30	69.72 Ga 31	72.59 Ge 32	74.922 As 33	78.96 Se 34	79.904 Br 35	83.80 Kr 36
5	85.468 Rb 37	87.62 Sr 38	88.906 Y 39	91.22 Zr 40	92.9064 Nb 41	95.94 Mo 42	98.906 Tc 43	101.07 Ru 44	102.906 Rh 45	106.4 Pd 46	107.868 Ag 47	112.41 Cd 48	114.82 In 49	118.69 Sn 50	121.75 Sb 51	127.60 Te 52	126.904 I 53	131.30 Xe 54
6	132.906 Cs 55	137.33 Ba 56	138.906 *La 57	178.49 Hf 72	180.948 Ta 73	183.85 W 74	186.2 Re 75	190.2 Os 76	192.22 Ir 77	195.09 Pt 78	196.967 Au 79	200.59 Hg 80	204.37 Tl 81	207.2 Pb 82	208.981 Bi 83	(209) Po 84	(210) At 85	(222) Rn 86
7	(223) Fr 87	226.025 Ra 88	(227) **Ac 89	(261) Rf 104	(262) Ha 105	263 Unh 106	(262) Uns 107	(265) Uno 108	(266) Une 109									

*Lanthanide series

140.12 Ce 58	140.908 Pr 59	144.24 Nd 60	(145) Pm 61	150.4 Sm 62	151.96 Eu 63	157.25 Gd 64	158.925 Tb 65	162.50 Dy 66	164.930 Ho 67	167.26 Er 68	168.934 Tm 69	173.04 Yb 70	174.967 Lu 71

**Actinide series

232.038 Th 90	231.031 Pa 91	238.029 U 92	237.048 Np 93	(244) Pu 94	(243) Am 95	(247) Cm 96	(247) Bk 97	(251) Cf 98	(254) Es 99	(257) Fm 100	(256) Md 101	(255) No 102	(257) Lr 103

FIGURE 7-1   A modern Periodic Table arranged into group of elements having similar properties.

In this experiment we will observe flame tests and solution reactions of selected alkali and alkaline earth elements. A *flame test* is a diagnostic test that is performed by placing a small amount of solution on the coiled tip of a wire and holding the wire over a hot flame to observe the color produced (Figure 7-2). For example, sodium solutions give a yellow flame test, copper solutions a green flame test, and the flame test for silver solutions is not visible.

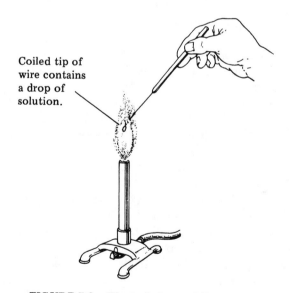

Coiled tip of wire contains a drop of solution.

FIGURE 7-2   The technique of flame testing.

Although flame tests are usually specific for each element, they can be misleading. Sodium is always present as an impurity. Therefore, a flame test will always give a yellow flame. However, the intensity of the yellow flame is less for an impurity than for a sodium compound and the distinction can be made with a little practice. Oftentimes the color of the flame test is similar for two different elements. In these cases, an element is confirmed by directly comparing the flame test of an unknown to a known solution.

EQUIPMENT AND CHEMICALS

Equipment

- 16 × 150 mm test tubes (6)
- test tube rack
- test tube brush
- flame test wire (chromel, nichrome, or platinum)
- wash bottle

Chemicals

- ammonium carbonate solution, 0.5 M $(NH_4)_2 CO_3$
- ammonium phosphate solution, 0.5 M $(NH_4)_2 HPO_4$
- ammonium sulfate solution, 0.5 M $(NH_4)_2 SO_4$
- Barium solution, 0.5 M $BaCl_2$

- Calcium solution, 0.5 M $CaCl_2$
- Lithium solution, 0.5 M LiCl
- Potassium solution, 0.5 M KCl
- Sodium solution, 0.5 M NaCl
- Strontium solution, 0.5 M $SrCl_2$
- Chloride solution, 0.5 M NaCl
- Bromide solution, 0.5 M NaBr
- Iodide solution, 0.5 M NaI
- hexane, C_6H_6
- dilute nitric acid, 6 M HNO_3
- chlorine water (bleach)
- unknown solutions containing one of the above alkali or alkaline earth elements and a halide, 0.5 M concentration

PROCEDURE

A. Flame Tests for the Alkali and Alkaline Earth Elements

1. Place six test tubes in a test tube rack. Add 2 mL (1/10 test tube) of the following solutions into separate test tubes: barium, calcium, lithium, potassium, sodium, strontium (see Figure 7-3).

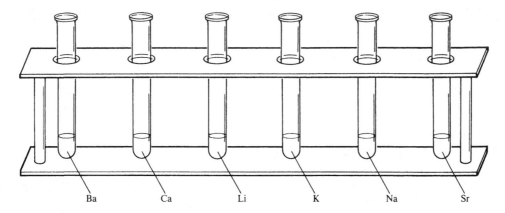

FIGURE 7-3   Test tube rack with solutions of alkali and alkaline earth elements.

2. Obtain a flame test wire and make a small loop in the end. Heat the loop with a burner at the tip of the blue cone. Continue to heat the wire until there is no longer any color produced in the flame. To avoid contamination, do not touch the clean wire.
3. Dip the clean wire into the test tube containing the barium solution. Place the loop at the tip of the flame. Record your observation. Clean the wire and repeat the flame test for the solutions containing calcium, lithium, potassium, sodium, and strontium.

NOTE: To clean a used wire, dip the wire in concentrated hydrochloric acid and heat the wire to red heat. In some instances, it may be necessary to repeat this operation.

B. Reactions of the Alkali and Alkaline Earth Elements

1. Add 1 mL of ammonium carbonate solution to each test tube. If a precipitate forms, record *ppt* in the Data Table. If there is no reaction, record *NR*.
2. Clean the test tubes and rinse with distilled water. Put 2 mL (1/10 test tube) of the barium, calcium, lithium, potassium, sodium, strontium solutions into separate test tubes. Add 1 mL of ammonium phosphate solution into each test tube. Record your observations in the Data Table.
3. Clean the test tubes and put 2 mL of the barium, calcium, lithium, potassium, sodium, and strontium solutions into separate test tubes. Add 1 mL of ammonium sulfate solution into each test tube and record your observations.

C. Reactions of the Halides

1. Place three test tubes in a test tube rack. Add 2 mL (1/10 test tube) of the following solutions into separate test tubes: chloride, bromide, iodide.
2. Into each test tube add 2 mL of hexane, 2 mL of chlorine water, and a drop of nitric acid.
3. Shake each test tube and observe the color of the upper hexane layer.

NOTE: Dispose of these solutions in a special waste container for organic chemicals.

D. Analysis of an Unknown Solution

1. Record the unknown number of a solution assigned by the instructor. Perform a flame test on the unknown solution and record your observation in the Data Table.
2. Put 2 mL of unknown solution into each of three test tubes. Add 1 mL of ammonium carbonate to the first; 1 mL of ammonium phosphate to the second; and 1 mL of ammonium sulfate to the third. Record your observations in the Data Table.
3. Put 2 mL of unknown solution into a test tube. Add 2 mL of hexane, 2 mL of chlorine water, and a drop of nitric acid. Shake the test tube and record the color of the upper hexane layer in the Data Table.
4. Compare the flame test and solution reactions of the unknown solution to the six known solutions (Procedures A and B). Deduce which of the alkali or alkaline earth elements is present in the unknown solution.
5. Compare the halide test of the unknown solution to the three known solutions (Procedure C). Deduce which of the halides is present in the unknown solution.

PRELABORATORY ASSIGNMENT*

1. In your own words define the following terms: alkali metals, alkaline earth metals, flame test, halide, immiscible, and precipitate.
2. In this experiment which three alkali elements are investigated? Which three alkaline earth elements? Which three halides?
3. What difficulties arise in interpreting a flame test?
4. Are water and hexane miscible? Which is the hexane layer? In which layer do you observe the halide test?
5. What safety precautions should be observed in this experiment?

*Answers in Appendix II.

NAME _____

SECTION _____

DATA TABLE FOR PERIODIC CLASSIFICATION OF THE ELEMENTS

A. Flame Tests for the Alkali and Alkaline Earth Elements

Solution tested

	Flame Test Observations
Barium	
Calcium	
Lithium	
Potassium	
Sodium	
Strontium	

B. Reactions of the Alkali and Alkaline Earth Elements

Solution tested	*Solution Reaction Observations*		
	ammonium carbonate	ammonium phosphate	ammonium sulfate
Barium			
Calcium			*
Lithium			
Potassium			
Sodium			
Strontium			

*Heat gently if there is no reaction.

C. Reactions of the Halides

Solution tested	*Observations of Upper Layer*
Chloride	
Bromide	
Iodide	

D. Analysis of an Unknown Solution   UNKNOWN # _____

Solution tested	*Flame Test Observation*
Unknown	

Solution tested	*Solution Reaction Observations*		
	ammonium carbonate	ammonium phosphate	ammonium sulfate
Unknown			

The unknown solution contains which of the following alkali or alkaline earth elements?

Barium   Calcium   Lithium   Potassium   Sodium   Strontium

Solution tested	*Observation of Upper Layer*
Unknown	

The unknown solution contains which of the following halides?

Chloride   Bromide   Iodide

NAME _____

1. Refer to Reactions of the Alkali and Alkaline Earth Elements in the Data Table (Procedure B).
    Which elements behave chemically similar to

    (a) barium   _____

    (b) sodium   _____

2. State the family name and designate the group number for each of the following:

    (a) barium   _____

    (b) sodium   _____

3. An unknown solution produced a crimson flame test with a few flashes of yellow. The solu-
    tion did not give a precipitate with ammonium carbonate, ammonium phosphate, or ammo-
    nium sulfate. The halide test produced a violet color in the hexane layer. Name the (a) alkali
    or alkaline earth element, and the (b) halide in the unknown solution.

    (a) _____   (b) _____

4. An unknown solution gave a green flame test that was brief. The solution produced a white
    precipitate with ammonium carbonate, ammonium phosphate, and ammonium sulfate. The
    halide test showed no discoloration of the hexane layer. Name the (a) alkali or alkaline
    earth element, and the (b) halide in the unknown solution.

    (a) _____   (b) _____

5. Yule logs are commercially available that burn with a red and green flame. What two chemi-
    cals could produce this effect?

6. For a family of elements, does the **metallic character** *increase* or *decrease* proceeding down a
    group?

7. For a family of elements, does the **atomic radius** *increase* or *decrease* proceeding down a
    group?

8. For a series of elements, does the **metallic character** *increase* or *decrease* proceeding left to
    right across a period?

9. For a series of elements, does the **atomic radius** *increase* or *decrease* proceeding left to right
    across a period?

10. Selected elements have been placed into a blank Periodic Table.

		IA	IIA	IIIB	IVB	VB	VIB	VIIB	VIII			IB	IIB	IIIA	IVA	VA	VIA	VIIA	0
1		H																	
2																		F	
3			Mg												Al					Ar
4										Co						As	Se		
5												Ag			Sn				
6		Cs											Hg						
7																			

				Pm													
					Pu												

Write the symbol of the element from the above Periodic Table that fits the following descriptions.

(a) an alkali metal   _____

(b) an alkaline earth metal   _____

(c) a halogen   _____

(d) a noble gas   _____

(e) a representative element in the fifth period   _____

(f) a transition element in the fifth period   _____

(g) a metalloid   _____

(h) a nonmetal left of the metalloids   _____

(i) a lanthanide   _____

(j) an actinide   _____

(k) atomic number 13   _____

(l) filling a 5d sublevel   _____

(m) electronic configuration: $1s^2\,2s^2\,2p^6\,3s^2\,3p^6\,4s^2\,3d^7$ _____

(n) six valence electrons   _____

11. (optional) Examine the Periodic Table on the last page of this manual. List three pairs of elements that are not arranged according to increasing atomic mass. (Ignore the elements in the actinide series.)

(a) _____ / _____

(b) _____ / _____

(c) _____ / _____

4

Specific Heat of a Metal

OBJECTIVES

1. To determine the specific heat of metallic aluminum.
2. To determine the specific heat of an unknown metal.
3. To gain practical experience in measuring temperature changes in a calorimeter.

DISCUSSION

One of the properties of matter is that it requires a certain amount of heat energy to raise the temperature of a unit mass of a substance. This property is termed the *specific heat* of a substance. In the metric system the specific heat of a substance is the amount of heat energy necessary to raise 1.00 g of that substance $1.00°C$.

Heat energy is measured in units of calories (cal) or kilocalories (kcal). A calorie is the amount of heat necessary to raise the temperature of 1.00 g of water $1.00°C$. Thus, we say that the specific heat of water is 1.00 calorie per gram per degree Celsius.

$$\text{specific heat of water} = \frac{1.00 \text{ cal}}{1 \text{ g} \times 1°C} \text{ or } 1.00 \text{ cal/g} \times °C$$

One of the properties of metals is that they are good conductors of heat. It therefore follows that metals have low specific heats as it requires less heat to raise their temperatures.

In this experiment we wish to find the specific heat of a metal. If a heated sample of hot metal is dropped into a styrofoam cup containing cool water, the temperature of the metal decreases and the temperature of the water increases. As a matter of fact, if we assume that no heat escapes from the cup, then the heat loss of the metal is equal to the heat gain by the water.

$$\text{heat loss of metal} = \text{heat gain of water}$$

From the temperature changes of the metal and water, we can calculate the specific heat of the metal.

PROBLEM EXAMPLE 4-1

A 50.05 g sample of zinc metal at 99.5°C was dropped into a styrofoam cup containing 100.0 g of water at 21.0°C. The water in the cup reached a maximum temperature of 24.5°. Calculate the specific heat of the metal.

Solution: First, let us calculate the heat gain of the water.

$$\frac{1.00 \text{ cal}}{1\,g \times 1°C} \times 100.0\,g \times (24.5 - 21.0)°C = 350 \text{ cal}$$

Since the temperature change, 3.5°C, represents only two significant digits, the final answer is limited to two significant digits.

The heat gain of the water is 350 calories; hence, the heat loss of the metal must be 350 calories (assuming no other heat losses to the environment). The heat loss for the sample over the temperature drop interval is

$$\frac{350 \text{ cal}}{50.05\,g \times (99.5 - 24.5)°C} = \frac{350 \text{ cal}}{50.05\,g \times 75.0°C} = 0.093 \text{ cal/}g \times °C$$

Experimentally, the metal will be first heated in a test tube immersed in a boiling waterbath; then the metal will be transferred into a styrofoam cup containing water at room temperature. Calorimeter is the technical term for a device where heat changes are measured. The styrofoam cup calorimeter and waterbath apparatus are shown in Figure 4-1.

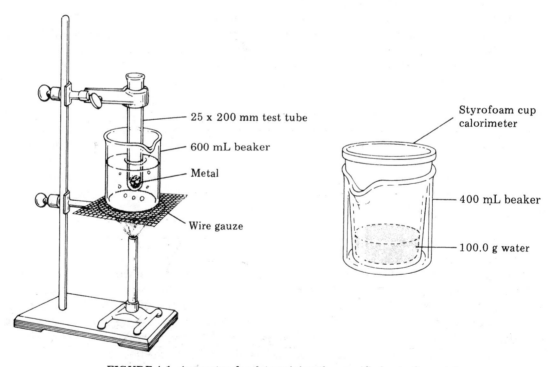

FIGURE 4-1 Apparatus for determining the specific heat of a metal.

EQUIPMENT AND CHEMICALS

- 250 mL beaker
- wire gauze
- utility clamp
- 25 × 200 mm test tube
- 600 mL beaker
- 110°C thermometer

- 100 mL graduated cylinder
- 400 mL beaker
- styrofoam cup
- aluminum rods or sticks (2 in. by 1/4 in.)
- unknown metal samples

PROCEDURE

A. Specific Heat of Aluminum

1. Place a 600 mL beaker on a wire gauze supported on a ring stand. Add about 300 mL of distilled water and bring to a boil.
2. Obtain the mass of a 250 mL beaker. Place about 50 g of aluminum rods into the beaker and weigh accurately.
3. Pour the metal rods into a 25 × 200 mm test tube and insert the test tube, suspended by a utility clamp, into the beaker of boiling water. Continue to boil the water while heating the metal (see Figure 4-1).
4. Place a styrofoam cup into a 400 mL beaker for support. From a graduated cylinder, pour 100.0 mL of water into the cup. Record the *mass* of the water.

   NOTE: Recall that the density of water is 1.00 g/mL. The mass of 100.0 mL of water would of course be 100.0 g.

5. Record the temperature of the water in the styrofoam cup.
6. Observe the temperature of the boiling water in the waterbath and record the temperature of the metal.

   NOTE: Assume the temperature of the boiling water to be the same as that of the metal. Since the thermometer is not calibrated, we cannot assume a temperature of precisely 100.0°C for boiling water.

7. Rapidly transfer the metal into the calorimeter. Stir the water in the calorimeter with the thermometer. Observe the temperature rise for several minutes and then record the maximum temperature.
8. Replace the calorimeter water, weigh out dry metal rods, and do a second trial.
9. Calculate the specific heat for each trial and the average value of both trials for the aluminum metal.

   NOTE: Dry the aluminum rods on a paper towel and return to the designated container.

B. Specific Heat of an Unknown Metal

1. Obtain an unknown metal sample from the instructor and record the unknown number.
2. Follow the previous procedure and determine the specific heat of the unknown metal.

   NOTE: After completing the experiment, dry and return the unknown metal sample to the designated container.

PRELABORATORY ASSIGNMENT*

1. In your own words define the following terms: calorie, calorimeter, specific heat.
2. What is the mass of 100.0 mL of water?
3. What is the value of the specific heat of water?
4. If the temperature change for the calorimeter water is less than ten degrees, how many significant digits are in the calculated value for specific heat?
5. A 55.50 g sample of aluminum at 99.0°C is placed in 100.0 g of water at 19.5°C, producing a maximum resulting temperature of 27.5°C. Calculate the specific heat of the aluminum sample.
6. What are the primary sources of error in this experiment?
7. What precautions must be observed in this experiment?

*Answers in Appendix II.

NAME _____

DATE _____

SECTION _____

DATA TABLE FOR SPECIFIC HEAT OF A METAL

A. Specific Heat of Aluminum

mass of beaker + metal	_____ g	_____ g
mass of beaker	_____ g	_____ g
mass of metal	_____ g	_____ g
mass of water	_____ g	_____ g
temperature of metal	_____ °C	_____ °C
initial temperature of calorimeter water	_____ °C	_____ °C
maximum temperature of calorimeter water	_____ °C	_____ °C

Show the calculation for the specific heat of metal for trial 1.

Specific heat of metal	_____ cal/g × °C	_____ cal/g × °C
Average specific heat of metal	_____ cal/g × °C	

B. **Specific Heat of an Unknown Metal**   UNKNOWN #_____

mass of beaker + metal   _____ g   _____ g

mass of beaker   _____ g   _____ g

mass of unknown metal   _____ g   _____ g

mass of water   _____ g   _____ g

temperature of unknown metal   _____ °C   _____ °C

initial temperature of
    calorimeter water   _____ °C   _____ °C

maximum temperature of
    calorimeter water   _____ °C   _____ °C

Show the calculation for specific heat for trial 1.

Specific heat of unknown metal   _____ cal/g × °C   _____ cal/g × °C

Average specific heat
    of unknown metal   _____ cal/g × °C

POSTLABORATORY ASSIGNMENT NAME ______________________

1. Calculate the number of kilocalories necessary to raise $25\bar{0}$ g of water from 19.6 to 68.8° C.

____

2. Calculate the mass of a piece of copper that released 125 calories when cooled from 100.0° C to 25.3° C. The specific heat of copper is 0.00924 cal/g × °C.

____

3. Find the specific heat of an unknown metal if a 35.5 g sample at 99.6° C produced a resulting temperature of 26.1° C when placed in a calorimeter containing 100.5 g of water at 20.2° C.

____

4. A 65.0 g sample of zinc (specific heat = 0.0922 cal/g × °C) was cooled from 100.0°C to 29.4°C in a calorimeter cup containing water initially at 21.5°C. Find the mass of water in the cup.

_____

5. (optional) Ignoring any heat loss to the surrounding environment, calculate the theoretical maximum temperature produced in a calorimeter containing 95.5 g of water at 20.8°C after a 25.0 g sample of aluminum (specific heat = 0.215 cal/g × °C) at 98.6°C has been introduced.

_____

5

Chemical Reactions

OBJECTIVES

1. To become familiar with the evidence for chemical reaction.
2. To translate word equations into balanced chemical equations.
3. To prepare metallic copper and determine the atomic mass of an unknown metal (M).
4. To systematically study five major types of reactions.

DISCUSSION

Ordinary chemical reactions can be considered to be one of five types. The first type is the synthesis of a single compound from two or more substances. This type of reaction is termed *combination*.

$$A + Z \longrightarrow AZ$$

A second type of reaction is termed *decomposition* in which a single compound breaks down into two or more simpler substances, usually by the application of heat.

$$AZ \longrightarrow A + Z$$

A third type of reaction is called *replacement*; here, one element simply displaces another from a compound. The element that is displaced is lower in the electromotive series.

$$A + BZ \longrightarrow AZ + B$$

In a *double replacement* reaction, two substances in solution switch partners; that is, the anion of one substance exchanges with the anion of another compound.

$$AX + BZ \longrightarrow AZ + BX$$

A fifth type of reaction is a *neutralization* reaction; an acid and a base react to form a salt and water.

$$HX + BOH \longrightarrow BX + HOH$$

A neutralization reaction is actually a special type of double replacement reaction, where one cation is hydrogen and one anion is hydroxide. The hydrogen in the acid neutralizes the hydroxide in the base to form water. If the formula of water is written as HOH, the equation is more easily balanced.

In this experiment, each of the five types of reactions is performed. The evidence of reaction is carefully observed and recorded. The evidence may include any of the following: (1) a gas is produced; (2) a precipitate is formed; (3) a color change is observed; (4) a temperature change is noted.

There are many symbols used in chemical equations to convey the reaction conditions. Table 14-1 lists some of these.

TABLE 14-1 Symbols in Chemical Equations

Symbol	Translation
$\longrightarrow$	produces, yields (separates reactants from products)
+	added to, reacts with (separates two or more reactants or products)
Δ	heat catalyst (written above $\longrightarrow$)
NR	no reaction (written after $\longrightarrow$)
(s)	solid or precipitate
(ℓ)	liquid
(g)	gas
(aq)	aqueous solution

In order to write an equation it is necessary to predict the products from a given reaction. Initially, this is a difficult task. To aid you in writing equations, word equations are supplied for each reaction. However, it is necessary to translate the word equations into balanced chemical equations. The following examples will illustrate.

EXAMPLE 14-1 COMBINATION REACTION

$$\text{zinc}_{(s)} + \text{oxygen}_{(g)} \xrightarrow{\Delta} \text{zinc oxide}_{(s)}$$

$$2\ Zn_{(s)} + O_{2(g)} \xrightarrow{\Delta} 2\ ZnO_{(s)}$$

EXAMPLE 14-2 DECOMPOSITION REACTION

$$\text{nickel(II) chloride hexahydrate}_{(s)} \xrightarrow{\Delta} \text{nickel(II) chloride}_{(s)} + \text{water}_{(g)}$$

$$NiCl_2 \cdot 6H_2O_{(s)} \xrightarrow{\Delta} NiCl_{2(s)} + 6\ H_2O_{(g)}$$

EXAMPLE 14-3 REPLACEMENT REACTION

$$\text{tin}_{(s)} + \text{hydrochloric acid}_{(aq)} \longrightarrow \text{tin(II) chloride}_{(aq)} + \text{hydrogen}_{(g)}$$

$$Sn_{(s)} + 2\ HCl_{(aq)} \longrightarrow SnCl_{2(aq)} + H_{2(g)}$$

EXAMPLE 14-4 DOUBLE REPLACEMENT REACTION

$$\text{potassium carbonate}_{(aq)} + \text{calcium chloride}_{(aq)} \longrightarrow \text{calcium carbonate}_{(s)} + \text{potassium chloride}_{(aq)}$$

$$K_2CO_{3(aq)} + CaCl_{2(aq)} \longrightarrow CaCO_{3(s)} + 2\ KCl_{(aq)}$$

EXAMPLE 14-5 NEUTRALIZATION REACTION

hydrochloric acid$_{(aq)}$ + barium hydroxide$_{(aq)}$ $\longrightarrow$ barium chloride$_{(aq)}$ + water$_{(\ell)}$

$$2\ HCl_{(aq)} + Ba(OH)_{2\,(aq)} \longrightarrow BaCl_{2\,(aq)} + 2\ HOH_{(\ell)}$$

Also in this experiment you will prepare metallic copper using an unknown metal. The unknown metal *(M)* displaces copper from a copper sulfate solution as follows:

$$M_{(s)} + CuSO_{4\,(aq)} \longrightarrow MSO_{4\,(aq)} + Cu_{(s)}$$

The mass of solid copper produced is compared to the mass of unknown metal.

PROBLEM EXAMPLE 14-1

A student weighed out 0.367 g of unknown metal *(M)*. After reaction with 25 mL of copper sulfate solution, 0.417 g of metallic copper was collected. Calculate the atomic mass of the unknown metal. The equation for the reaction is shown above.

Solution: From the chemical equation, we see one mole of *M* produces one mole of Cu.

$$0.417\ g\ Cu \times \frac{1\ mole\ Cu}{63.5\ g\ Cu} \times \frac{1\ mole\ M}{1\ mole\ Cu} = 0.00657\ mol\ M$$

The atomic mass (g/mole) is:

$$\frac{0.367\ g\ M}{0.00657\ mol\ M} = 55.9\ g/mole$$

In this example the atomic mass is found to be 55.9 g/mole, which corresponds to iron. Other unknown metals *(M)* will give a different value.

EQUIPMENT AND CHEMICALS

Equipment

- crucible tongs
- evaporating dish
- 100 mL graduated cylinder
- 250 mL beaker
- wire gauze
- 16 × 150 mm test tubes (6)
- test tube holder
- test tube brush
- 250 mL Erlenmeyer flask
- crucible
- wash bottle

Chemicals

- magnesium, Mg ribbon
- sulfur, S powder
- zinc, Zn powder
- copper(II) sulfate pentahydrate, solid $CuSO_4 \cdot 5H_2O$
- sodium hydrogen carbonate, solid $NaHCO_3$

- wooden splints
- copper, Cu wire
- calcium, Ca turnings
- dilute hydrochloric acid, 6 M HCl
- silver nitrate, 0.1 M $AgNO_3$
- mercury(II) nitrate, 0.1 M $Hg(NO_3)_2$
- aluminum nitrate, 0.1 M $Al(NO_3)_3$
- potassium iodide, 0.1 M KI
- sodium phosphate, 0.1 M Na_3PO_4
- nitric acid, 0.1 M HNO_3
- sulfuric acid, 0.1 M H_2SO_4
- phosphoric acid, 0.1 M H_3PO_4
- sodium hydroxide, 0.1 M NaOH
- phenolphthalein
- copper(II) sulfate, 0.5 M $CuSO_4$
- unknown metal samples

PROCEDURE

NOTE: For Procedures A-E, record your observations in the Data Table. On the page following the observations, word equations are written for each reaction. Write the corresponding balanced chemical equation.

For Procedure F, the unknown metal may require 30 minutes for complete reaction. Therefore, it may be convenient to perform the first two steps of Procedure F before beginning Procedures A-E.

A. Combination Reactions

1. Hold a 2 cm strip of magnesium ribbon with crucible tongs and ignite the metal in a hot burner flame.
2. Mix together 2 g of powdered zinc and 1 g of sulfur in a crucible and place under a fume hood. Heat the end of a metal wire to red heat and use the end to ignite the mixture.

   CAUTION: The instructor should either demonstrate or closely supervise this reaction. This procedure should be considered dangerous.

B. Decomposition Reactions

1. Add a few crystals of copper(II) sulfate pentahydrate in a dry test tube. Holding the test tube with a test tube holder, heat strongly with a burner. Note the change in color and texture and observe the inside wall of the test tube.
2. Add sodium hydrogen carbonate (baking soda) into a 250 mL Erlenmeyer flask so as to sparsely cover the bottom. Support the flask on a ring stand using a wire gauze.
   (a) Hold a lighted splint inside the neck of the flask and observe how long it burns.
   (b) Heat the flask strongly with the burner and note the inside wall of the flask. After moisture collects, plunge a flaming splint into the flask and observe how long it burns.

C. Replacement Reactions

1. Put 2 mL (about 1/10 test tube) of silver nitrate into a test tube and add a small copper wire. Allow a few minutes for reaction and then record your observation.
2. Place a small piece of magnesium into a test tube containing about 2 mL of dilute hydrochloric acid.
3. Place a small piece of calcium metal into a test tube containing a few milliliters of distilled water.

D. Double Replacement Reactions

1. Put 2 mL of silver nitrate, mercury(II) nitrate, and aluminum nitrate into separate test tubes #1-3. Add about 2 mL of potassium iodide into test tube #1 and check for evidence of reaction.
2. Add about 2 mL of potassium iodide into test tube #2 and check for reaction.
3. Add about 2 mL of potassium iodide into test tube #3 and check for reaction.
4. Put 2 mL of silver nitrate, mercury(II) nitrate, and aluminum nitrate into separate test tubes #4-6. Add about 2 mL of sodium phosphate into test tube #4 and check for evidence of reaction.
5. Add about 2 mL of sodium phosphate into test tube #5 and note the reaction.
6. Add about 2 mL of sodium phosphate into test tube #6 and observe the reaction.

E. Neutralization Reactions

1. Put 2 mL of nitric acid, sulfuric acid, and phosphoric acid into separate test tubes #1-3. Introduce one drop of phenolphthalein indicator into each of the test tubes. Add sodium hydroxide solution to test tube #1 until a permanent color change is observed.

   NOTE: Phenolphthalein is an acid-base indicator that is colorless in acidic and neutral solutions and pink in basic solutions.

2. Add sodium hydroxide solution into test tube #2 until a permanent color change is observed.
3. Add sodium hydroxide solution into test tube #3 until a permanent color change is observed.

F. Preparation of Copper from an Unknown Metal

1. Weigh a clean, dry evaporating dish. Add 0.2-0.5 g of unknown metal into the dish and reweigh. Find the mass of the metal by difference.
2. Using a graduated cylinder, pour 25 mL of copper(II) sulfate solution into the evaporating dish. Allow the unknown metal to react completely with the copper solution.

   NOTE: It may be convenient to stop at this step and complete Procedures A-E.

3. After the reaction is complete, carefully pour off the solution so that the copper metal remains in the dish. A small amount of blue solution will remain also.
4. Wash the copper metal with 25 mL of distilled water and discard the washings. Repeat the washing procedure until the copper metal is clear of blue solution.
5. Prepare a waterbath in a 250 mL beaker and place the evaporating dish in the beaker (Figure 14-1). Evaporate the copper metal to dryness.

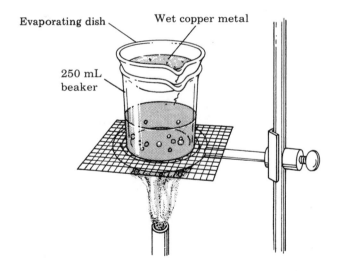

FIGURE 14-1   Apparatus for drying the metallic copper.

6. After evaporation, remove the dish and wipe dry. Hold the dish with crucible tongs over a flame to remove the last traces of moisture. Allow the dish to cool and weigh the evaporating dish with residue.
7. Calculate the atomic mass (g/mole) of the unknown metal (*M*). Identify the metal (*M*) from its atomic mass.

PRELABORATORY ASSIGNMENT*

1. In your own words define the following terms: catalyst, electromotive series, exothermic reaction, precipitate, product, reactant.
2. Explain the meaning of the following symbols:

   $\xrightarrow{\Delta}$, NR, (s), (ℓ), (g), (aq)
3. List four observations that are evidence of chemical reaction.
4. What is the estimated volume of liquid in a test tube that is 1/10 full?
5. What color is the phenolphthalein indicator in an acid solution? In a basic solution?
6. What safety precautions should be followed in this experiment?
7. Calculate the atomic mass of an unknown metal (M) given the following data:

mass of evaporating dish + unknown metal (M) =	45.882 g
mass of evaporating dish	= 45.361 g
mass of evaporating dish + copper metal	= 45.781 g

*Answers in Appendix II.

NAME _____

SECTION _____

DATA TABLE FOR CHEMICAL REACTIONS

Procedure	*Evidence of Reaction*
A. Combination Reactions	
1. $Mg + O_2 \xrightarrow{\Delta}$ $2MgO$	
2. $Zn + S \xrightarrow{\Delta}$ ZnS	
B. Decomposition Reactions	
1. $CuSO_4 \cdot 5H_2O \xrightarrow{\Delta}$ $CuSO_4 + 5H_2O$	
2. $2\,NaHCO_3 \xrightarrow{\Delta}$ $NaCO_3 + H_2O + CO_2$	
C. Replacement Reactions	
1. $Cu + AgNO_3 \longrightarrow$	
2. $Mg + HCl \longrightarrow$	
3. $Ca + H_2O \longrightarrow$	
D. Double Replacement Reactions	
1. $AgNO_3 + KI \longrightarrow$	
2. $Hg(NO_3)_2 + KI \longrightarrow$	
3. $Al(NO_3)_3 + KI \longrightarrow$	
4. $AgNO_3 + Na_3PO_4 \longrightarrow$	
5. $Hg(NO_3)_2 + Na_3PO_4 \longrightarrow$	
6. $Al(NO_3)_3 + Na_3PO_4 \longrightarrow$	
E. Neutralization Reactions	
1. $HNO_3 + NaOH \longrightarrow$	
2. $H_2SO_4 + NaOH \longrightarrow$	
3. $H_3PO_4 + NaOH \longrightarrow$	

Translate Each Word Equation Into a Balanced Chemical Equation

A. Combination Reactions

1. magnesium metal$_{(s)}$ + oxygen$_{(g)}$ $\xrightarrow{\Delta}$ magnesium oxide$_{(s)}$

2. zinc metal$_{(s)}$ + sulfur$_{(s)}$ $\xrightarrow{\Delta}$ zinc sulfide$_{(s)}$

B. Decomposition Reactions

1. copper(II) sulfate pentahydrate$_{(s)}$ $\xrightarrow{\Delta}$ copper(II) sulfate$_{(s)}$ + water$_{(g)}$

2. sodium hydrogen carbonate$_{(s)}$ $\xrightarrow{\Delta}$ sodium carbonate$_{(s)}$ + water$_{(\ell)}$ + carbon dioxide$_{(g)}$

C. Replacement Reactions

1. copper metal$_{(s)}$ + silver nitrate$_{(aq)}$ $\longrightarrow$ copper(II) nitrate$_{(aq)}$ + silver metal$_{(s)}$

2. magnesium metal$_{(s)}$ + hydrochloric acid$_{(aq)}$ $\longrightarrow$ magnesium chloride$_{(aq)}$ + hydrogen$_{(g)}$

3. calcium metal$_{(s)}$ + water$_{(\ell)}$ $\longrightarrow$ calcium hydroxide$_{(s)}$ + hydrogen$_{(g)}$

D. Double Replacement Reactions

1. silver nitrate$_{(aq)}$ + potassium iodide$_{(aq)}$ $\longrightarrow$ silver iodide$_{(s)}$ + potassium nitrate$_{(aq)}$

2. mercury(II) nitrate$_{(aq)}$ + potassium iodide$_{(aq)}$ $\longrightarrow$ mercury(II) iodide$_{(s)}$ + potassium nitrate$_{(aq)}$

3. aluminum nitrate$_{(aq)}$ + potassium iodide$_{(aq)}$ $\longrightarrow$ no reaction

4. silver nitrate$_{(aq)}$ + sodium phosphate$_{(aq)}$ $\longrightarrow$ silver phosphate$_{(s)}$ + sodium nitrate$_{(aq)}$

5. mercury(II) nitrate$_{(aq)}$ + sodium phosphate$_{(aq)}$ $\longrightarrow$ mercury(II) phosphate$_{(s)}$ + sodium nitrate$_{(aq)}$

6. aluminum nitrate$_{(aq)}$ + sodium phosphate$_{(aq)}$ $\longrightarrow$ aluminum phosphate$_{(s)}$ + sodium nitrate$_{(aq)}$

E. Neutralization Reactions

1. nitric acid$_{(aq)}$ + sodium hydroxide$_{(aq)}$ $\longrightarrow$ sodium nitrate$_{(aq)}$ + water$_{(\ell)}$

2. sulfuric acid$_{(aq)}$ + sodium hydroxide$_{(aq)}$ $\longrightarrow$ sodium sulfate$_{(aq)}$ + water$_{(\ell)}$

3. phosphoric acid$_{(aq)}$ + sodium hydroxide$_{(aq)}$ $\longrightarrow$ sodium phosphate$_{(aq)}$ + water$_{(\ell)}$

1. Identify the chemical formula for each of the following substances. Refer to your observations in the Data Table along with the corresponding word equations.

    (a) white smoke (Procedure **A.1**)   _____

    (b) colorless liquid (Procedure **B.1**)   _____

    (c) flame-extinguishing gas (Procedure **B.2**)   _____

    (d) gray solid (Procedure **C.1**)   _____

    (e) colorless gas (Procedure **C.2**)   _____

    (f) orange ppt. (Procedure **D.2**)   _____

    (g) yellow ppt. (Procedure **D.4**)   _____

    (h) white ppt. (Procedure **D.6**)   _____

2. Change the following word equations to balanced chemical equations.

    (a) copper metal + oxygen $\xrightarrow{\Delta}$ copper(II) oxide

    (b) mercury(I) nitrate + potassium bromide $\longrightarrow$ mercury(I) bromide + potassium nitrate

    (c) aluminum metal + sulfuric acid $\longrightarrow$ aluminum sulfate + hydrogen

    (d) acetic acid + barium hydroxide $\longrightarrow$ barium acetate + water

    (e) iron(III) carbonate $\xrightarrow{\Delta}$ iron(III) oxide + carbon dioxide

    (f) sodium metal + water $\longrightarrow$ sodium hydroxide + hydrogen

    (g) calcium chloride dihydrate $\xrightarrow{\Delta}$ calcium chloride + water

    (h) bismuth sulfate + potassium chromate $\longrightarrow$ bismuth chromate + potassium sulfate

3. Circle any of the following compounds that are insoluble in water. Refer to the general solubility rules in Appendix VIII.

    (a) AgCl   (b) $Fe(OH)_3$

    (c) $Pb(NO_3)_2$ (d) $ZnCO_3$

    (e) $MgSO_4$ (f) $Ni_3(PO_4)_2$

    (g) $(NH_4)_2 CrO_4$ (h) CuS

    (i) $Ca(C_2H_3O_2)_2$ (j) HgO

4. Complete and balance the following single replacement reactions. If there is no reaction, write *NR*. Refer to the Electromotive Series in Appendix IX.

    (a) $Hg_{(\ell)}$ + $Fe(NO_3)_{3(aq)}$ $\longrightarrow$

    (b) $Zn_{(s)}$ + $Ni(C_2H_3O_2)_{2(aq)}$ $\longrightarrow$

    (c) $Al_{(s)}$ + $HCl_{(aq)}$ $\longrightarrow$

    (d) $Cu_{(s)}$ + $H_2SO_{4(aq)}$ $\longrightarrow$

5. (optional) Complete and balance the following equations.

    (a) $Pb(NO_3)_{2(aq)}$ + $K_2CrO_{4(aq)}$ $\longrightarrow$

    (b) $Zn(HCO_3)_{2(s)}$ $\xrightarrow{\Delta}$

    (c) $HC_2H_3O_{2(aq)}$ + $NH_3 \cdot H_2O_{(aq)}$ $\longrightarrow$

    (d) $Li_{(s)}$ + $Cl_{2(g)}$ $\xrightarrow{\Delta}$

    (e) $Mg_{(s)}$ + $SnF_{2(aq)}$ $\longrightarrow$

6

Empirical Formula

OBJECTIVES

1. To determine the empirical formula for magnesium oxide.
2. To determine the empirical formula for copper sulfide.
3. To gain practical experience in developing techniques using a crucible.

DISCUSSION

Empirical formula is defined as the simplest whole number ratio of the elements in a compound. The actual formula for the elements in a compound is termed the *molecular formula* and is the true ratio. For example, hydrogen peroxide has an actual formula of H_2O_2. The simplest ratio of the elements is H_1O_1 and therefore is the empirical formula. Acetylene is a gas used in welding and benzene is a liquid solvent. They have different physical and chemical properties, although both have the same empirical formula, C_1H_1. The molecular formula of acetylene is C_2H_2, whereas the molecular formula of benzene is C_6H_6.

Historically, empirical formulas were determined from the combining weight ratios of elements. This was a critical step in demonstrating the periodic properties of the elements. Empirical formula experiments were also performed in order to determine the combining capacity of the elements. Recently the synthetic element lawrencium was found to have a combining capacity of 3 from an empirical formula experiment. Radioactive lawrencium combined with chlorine to form lawrencium chloride which has the formula $LrCl_3$.

Some elements exhibit more than one combining capacity, and the empirical formula of the compound will depend on how the element combines. For instance, iron can react with oxygen to form either iron(II) oxide or iron(III) oxide, depending on experimental conditions.

PROBLEM EXAMPLE 13-1

A 0.279 g sample of iron was heated and allowed to react with oxygen from the air. The resulting product has a mass of 0.400 g. Find the experimental empirical formula for iron oxide.

Solution: The empirical formula is the whole number ratio of iron and oxygen in the compound iron oxide. This ratio is experimentally determined from the moles of each reactant. The moles of iron are calculated as

$$0.279 \text{ g Fe} \times \frac{1 \text{ mole Fe}}{55.8 \text{ g Fe}} = 0.00500 \text{ mole Fe}$$

The moles of oxygen is calculated after finding the mass of oxygen reacting.

$$0.400 \text{ g iron oxide} - 0.279 \text{ g Fe} = 0.121 \text{ g O}$$

$$0.121 \text{ g O} \times \frac{1 \text{ mole O}}{16.0 \text{ g O}} = 0.00756 \text{ mole O}$$

The mole ratio of the elements in iron oxide is

$$Fe_{0.00500} O_{0.00756}$$

We always divide by the smaller number in order to find the simplest whole number ratio:

$$Fe_{\frac{0.00500}{0.00500}} O_{\frac{0.00756}{0.00500}} = Fe_{1.00} O_{1.51}$$

Since we do not have whole numbers it is necessary to double the ratio: $Fe_2O_{3.02}$. The slight variation from a whole number ratio is accounted for by experimental error. The empirical formula is Fe_2O_3; the compound is iron(III) oxide.

PROBLEM EXAMPLE 13-2

A 1.226 sample of lead shot was placed in a crucible and covered with powdered sulfur. The crucible was heated until all the excess sulfur was driven off. The product weighed 1.417 g. What is the empirical formula of lead sulfide?

Solution: First we will calculate the moles of lead in the product.

$$1.226 \text{ g Pb} \times \frac{1 \text{ mole Pb}}{207 \text{ g Pb}} = 0.00592 \text{ mole Pb}$$

Second we will calculate the moles of sulfur that combined with the lead.

$$1.417 \text{ g lead sulfide} - 1.226 \text{ g Pb} = 0.191 \text{ g S}$$

$$0.191 \text{ g S} \times \frac{1 \text{ mole S}}{32.1 \text{ g S}} = 0.00595 \text{ moles S}$$

The mole ratio of the elements in lead sulfide is

$$Pb_{0.00592} S_{0.00595}$$

To simplify we divide by the smaller value:

$$Pb_{\frac{0.00592}{0.00592}} S_{\frac{0.00595}{0.00592}} = Pb_{1.00} S_{1.01}$$

The empirical formula of the product is PbS. The product is lead(II) sulfide.

In this experiment magnesium ribbon will be heated in a crucible and converted to an oxide product. The second part of the experiment involves the conversion of copper to copper sulfide. Since copper can form either copper(I) sulfide or copper(II) sulfide, the empirical formula is unknown and cannot be predicted. Figure 13-1 illustrates the experimental equipment.

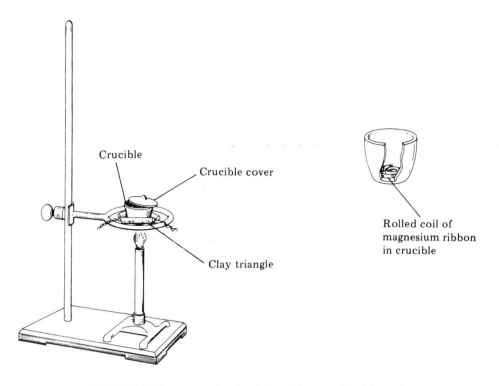

Crucible

Crucible cover

Clay triangle

Rolled coil of
magnesium ribbon
in crucible

FIGURE 13-1   Apparatus for determining empirical formula.

EQUIPMENT AND CHEMICALS

Equipment

- clay triangle
- crucible tongs
- crucible and cover

Chemicals

- magnesium, Mg ribbon
- copper, #18 gauge Cu wire
- sulfur, S powder

PROCEDURE

A. Empirical Formula of Magnesium Oxide

1. Support a crucible and cover with a clay triangle and place on a ring stand. Fire to red heat.
2. Remove the heat and allow the crucible to cool for 10 minutes. Using crucible tongs, transfer the crucible to the balance and find the mass.
3. Cut a 25 cm strip of magnesium ribbon and roll it into a flat coil. Place the loosely coiled magnesium flat against the bottom of the crucible and reweigh.
4. Return the crucible to the clay triangle. With the lid off, heat the crucible until the magnesium sparks and begins to smoke. Immediately remove the heat and place the cover firmly on the crucible using the tongs.

    NOTE: Safety goggles should be worn when heating the magnesium without the crucible lid.

5. After the smoke has ceased, continue to heat the crucible until the metal is completely converted to a gray-black residue. The progress of conversion can be checked periodically by removing the heat and raising the cover with the tongs.

6. When the metal no longer sparks, remove the heat and allow the crucible to cool for 10 minutes. Add several drops of distilled water with a dropper pipet to the residue.

   NOTE: Some of the magnesium will react with the nitrogen in the air forming magnesium nitride. The addition of water decomposes any magnesium nitride present releasing ammonia gas.

7. Refire to red heat for 5 minutes. Remove the heat and allow the crucible with product to cool for 10 minutes. Transfer the crucible to the balance and find the mass of the crucible and magnesium oxide.

8. Clean the crucible, repeat the procedure, and calculate the empirical formula for each trial.

B. Empirical Formula of Copper Sulfide

1. Support a crucible and cover with a clay triangle and place on a ring stand. Fire to red heat.

2. Remove the heat and allow the crucible to cool for 10 minutes. Using crucible tongs, transfer the crucible to the balance and find the mass.

3. Cut a 25 cm length of copper wire. Roll the wire into a coil, place it in the crucible, and reweigh.

4. Completely cover the copper with powdered sulfur. Place the lid on the crucible and gradually heat to red heat under a fume hood. Continue to heat for several minutes after the last trace of burning sulfur disappears. Holding the burner in your hand, heat the entire outside surface of the crucible and cover.

5. Allow the crucible and contents to cool for 10 minutes. Transfer the crucible to a balance and weigh the crucible, cover, and copper sulfide.

6. Clean the crucible, repeat the procedure, and calculate the empirical formula for each trial.

PRELABORATORY ASSIGNMENT*

1. In your own words define the following terms: empirical formula, firing to red heat, heating to constant weight, molecular formula, weighing by difference.
2. Why are crucible tongs used to transfer the crucible after heating and before weighing?
3. How critical are the suggested times for heating and cooling?
4. Why is distilled water added to the crucible after the initial heating of the magnesium?
5. How can you tell when the reaction is complete for the magnesium?
6. How can you tell when the copper has reacted completely and the excess sulfur is burned off?
7. What are the major sources of error in this experiment?
8. What safety precautions must be observed in this experiment?

*Answers in Appendix II.

DATA TABLE FOR EMPIRICAL FORMULA

A. **Empirical Formula of Magnesium Oxide**

mass of crucible and cover + magnesium
(before heating)   _____ g   _____ g

mass of crucible and cover   _____ g   _____ g

mass of magnesium   _____ g   _____ g

mass of crucible and cover + magnesium
oxide *(after heating)*   _____ g   _____ g

mass of combined oxygen   _____ g   _____ g

Show the calculation of empirical formula for trial 1.

Empirical formula of magnesium oxide   _____   _____

POSTLABORATORY ASSIGNMENT NAME ____________________

1. A 0.750 g sample of tin is oxidized with nitric acid to form tin oxide. Calculate the empirical formula of tin oxide if the original tin sample gained 0.201 g of oxygen.

____

2. Excess sulfur reacts with 0.565 g of cobalt to give 1.027 g of cobalt sulfide. Find the empirical formula of the product.

____

3. If 1.164 g of iron filings react with chlorine gas to give 3.384 g of iron chloride, what is the empirical formula of the compound?

____

4. A 0.626 g sample of copper oxide was reduced to 0.500 g of copper metal by heating in a stream of hydrogen. Calculate the empirical formula of the copper oxide sample.

____

5. A sample of phosphorus weighing 0.500 g was ignited to phosphorus oxide in a stream of pure oxygen. The product has a mass of 1.145 g. Calculate the empirical formula. Find the molecular formula if a separate experiment yielded a molecular mass of approximately 285 amu for the phosphorus oxide.

Empirical formula _____

Molecular formula _____

6. (optional) Ethylene glycol, the main ingredient in permanent antifreeze, contains 38.7 percent carbon, 9.7 percent hydrogen, and 51.6 percent oxygen. Calculate the empirical and molecular formulas given a molecular mass of approximately 60 amu.

Empirical formula _____

Molecular formula _____

7

Analysis by Precipitation

OBJECTIVES

1. To precipitate potassium iodide with lead(II) nitrate and determine the percent yield of lead(II) iodide.
2. To determine the percentage of potassium iodide in an unknown mixture.
3. To gain proficiency in transferring and filtering a precipitate.

DISCUSSION

In this experiment potassium iodide will be precipitated from aqueous solution with lead(II) nitrate. The equation for the reaaction is:

$$2 \text{ KI}_{(aq)} + \text{Pb(NO}_3)_{2(aq)} \longrightarrow \text{PbI}_{2(s)} + 2 \text{ KNO}_{3(aq)}$$

The insoluble lead(II) iodide solid is collected in filter paper. The mass of the precipitate is referred to as the *actual yield* of lead(II) iodide. The *theoretical yield* of lead(II) iodide is the calculated amount of precipitate formed according to the stoichiometry of the reaction. It is assumed that all of the potassium iodide reactant has been converted to lead(II) iodide product. The *percent yield* is found by comparing the actual yield to the theoretical yield and expressing the ratio as a percentage.

PROBLEM EXAMPLE 16-1

Calculate the percent yield of lead(II) iodide if 0.995 g of potassium iodide gives an actual yield of 1.141 g precipitate.

Solution: The above balanced equation for the reaction relates the mass of reactant to the precipitate. Given the formula mass of potassium iodide (166.0 amu) and lead(II) iodide (461.0 amu), we can calculate the theoretical yield of precipitate as follows:

$$0.995 \text{ g KI} \times \frac{1 \text{ mole KI}}{166.0 \text{ g KI}} \times \frac{1 \text{ mole PbI}_2}{2 \text{ moles KI}} \times \frac{461.0 \text{ g PbI}_2}{1 \text{ mole PbI}_2} = 1.38 \text{ g PbI}_2$$

The actual yield is given as 1.141 g PbI_2; therefore, the percent yield is found as follows:

$$\frac{\text{actual yield}}{\text{theoretical yield}} \times 100 = \% \text{ yield}$$

$$\frac{1.141 \text{ g}}{1.38 \text{ g}} \times 100 = 82.6\%$$

The second part of this experiment analyzes an unknown mixture for its potassium iodide content. Potassium iodide in the unknown sample is precipitated as before, forming insoluble lead(II) iodide. The equation for the reaction is the same as above and the stoichiometry calculations are similar.

PROBLEM EXAMPLE 16-2

Calculate the percentage of potassium iodide in a 1.005 g unknown mixture that produced a 0.915 g precipitate of lead(II) iodide.

Solution: As before, the mass of precipitate can be related to the mass of potassium iodide in the balanced equation. In this example the relationship is indirect as we relate the mass of product back to the mass of potassium iodide reactant.

$$0.915 \text{ g } PbI_2 \times \frac{1 \text{ mole } PbI_2}{461.0 \text{ g } PbI_2} \times \frac{2 \text{ moles KI}}{1 \text{ mole } PbI_2} \times \frac{166.0 \text{ g KI}}{1 \text{ mole KI}} = 0.659 \text{ g KI}$$

The percentage of KI in the unknown mixture is simply

$$\frac{\text{mass KI}}{\text{mass mixture}} \times 100 = \% \text{ yield}$$

$$\frac{0.659 \text{ g}}{1.005 \text{ g}} \times 100 = 65.5\%$$

Figure 16-1a shows the filtering apparatus before transferring the precipitate. Notice the lead(II) iodide has been allowed to settle out of solution before decanting the supernate. If the solution is transferred without allowing the precipitate to settle, the particles will prematurely clog the pores in the filter paper. This will slow the filtering process. Figure 16-1b illustrates washing the precipitate from the beaker into the filter paper.

EQUIPMENT AND CHEMICALS

Equipment

- 250 mL beaker
- 100 mL graduated cylinder
- wire gauze
- clay triangle
- funnel
- filter paper
- 400 mL beaker
- stirring rod
- rubber policeman
- wash bottle

Chemicals

- potassium iodide, anhydrous KI
- lead(II) nitrate solution, 0.1 M $Pb(NO_3)_2$
- unknown potassium iodide mixtures

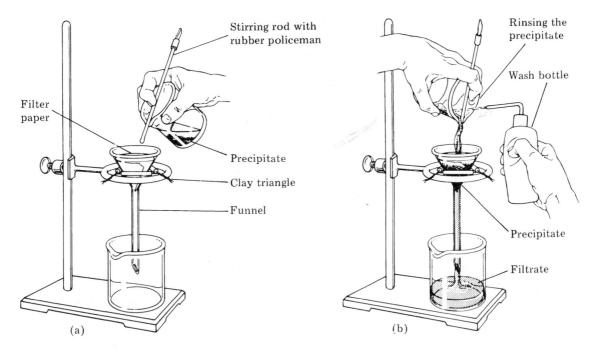

FIGURE 16-1 Filtering apparatus. (a) Allow the precipitate to settle, then pour off the supernate. (b) After the supernate passes through the filter paper, rinse the precipitate into the filter paper using a wash bottle.

PROCEDURE

A. Percent Yield of Lead(II) Iodide

1. Place a 250 mL beaker on the balance and record the mass. Add about 1 g potassium iodide (0.8–1.2 g) and reweigh accurately.
2. Dissolve the sample completely in 25 mL of distilled water. Using a graduated cylinder, transfer 50 mL of lead(II) nitrate solution into the 250 mL beaker.
3. Support the beaker with a wire gauze on a ring stand. Bring the solution to a gentle boil and then turn off the burner. Allow the precipitate to digest until the solution is cool.
4. Weigh a disk of filter paper. Prepare a filter paper cone as shown in Figure 16-2. Insert the filter paper cone into the funnel and moisten with water.

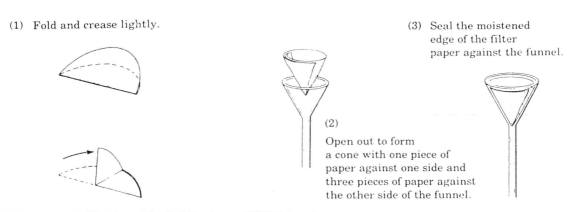

(1) Fold and crease lightly.

(3) Seal the moistened edge of the filter paper against the funnel.

(2) Open out to form a cone with one piece of paper against one side and three pieces of paper against the other side of the funnel.

FIGURE 16-2 Folding filter paper and inserting it into a funnel.

5. Assemble a filtering apparatus as shown in Figure 16-1.
6. Without disturbing the settled precipitate, carefully pour off the supernate into the filter paper. Use a stirring rod to guide the flow. Rinse out the bulk of the precipitate with a stream of water from the wash bottle. Clean the beaker using a rubber policeman and rinse the residue into the filter paper.

   NOTE: At no time add supernate above the top of the filter paper as precipitate particles can pass into the filtrate.

7. After all of the supernate has passed through the filter, carefully remove the paper cone from the funnel. After drying, weigh the filter paper with precipitate.
8. Calculate the theoretical yield of lead(II) iodide from the mass of the potassium iodide. Find the percent yield.

B. Percentage of Potassium Iodide in an Unknown Mixture

1. Obtain an unknown sample containing potassium iodide. Record the unknown number in the Data Table.
2. Repeat Steps 1-7 in the above procedure substituting the unknown mixture for potassium iodide.
3. Calculate the mass of potassium iodide in the unknown sample from the mass of precipitate. Find the percentage of potassium iodide in the unknown mixture.

PRELABORATORY ASSIGNMENT*

1. In your own words, define the following terms: actual yield, digestion, filtrate, percent yield, precipitate, stoichiometry, supernate, theoretical yield.
2. What problem arises if the precipitate is not allowed to settle completely from solution?
3. What is the purpose of the rubber policeman?
4. What should you do if particles of precipitate appear in the filtrate?
5. What are the primary sources of error in this experiment?
6. Is it possible to have a percent yield which is greater than 100%?
7. What safety precautions must be observed in this experiment?

*Answers in Appendix II.

NAME _____

SECTION _____

DATA TABLE FOR ANALYSIS BY PRECIPITATION

A. Percent Yield of Lead(II) Iodide

mass of beaker + KI   _____ g

mass of beaker   _____ g

mass of KI   _____ g

mass of filter paper + PbI_2 ppt   _____ g

mass of filter paper   _____ g

mass of PbI_2 ppt (actual yield)   _____ g

Show the calculation for the theoretical yield of lead(II) iodide.

mass of PbI_2 ppt (theoretical yield)   _____ g

Show the calculation for percent yield of lead(II) iodide.

Percent yield of PbI_2 _____ %

B. **Percentage of Potassium Iodide in an Unknown Mixture**

UNKNOWN # _____

mass of beaker + unknown mixture   _____ g

mass of beaker   _____ g

mass of unknown mixture   _____ g

mass of filter paper + PbI_2 ppt   _____ g

mass of filter paper   _____ g

mass of PbI_2 ppt   _____ g

Show the calculation for the mass of potassium iodide in the unknown mixture.

mass of KI   _____ g

Show the calculation for percentage of potassium iodide in the unknown mixture.

Percentage of KI   _____ %

POSTLABORATORY ASSIGNMENT NAME ______________________

1. A 1.020 g sample of sodium fluoride is dissolved in water and then precipitated with calcium nitrate solution. If the calcium fluoride precipitate weighs 0.905 g, what is the percent yield?

$$2\ NaF_{(aq)} + Ca(NO_3)_{2\,(aq)} \longrightarrow CaF_{2\,(s)} + 2\ NaNO_{3\,(aq)}$$

____

2. The stannous fluoride in a 10.000 g sample of toothpaste was extracted and then precipitated with lanthanum nitrate solution. If the mass of the precipitate is 0.105 g, what is the percentage of stannous fluoride in the toothpaste sample?

$$3\ SnF_{2\,(aq)} + 2\ La(NO_3)_{3\,(aq)} \longrightarrow 2\ LaF_{3\,(s)} + 3\ Sn(NO_3)_{2\,(aq)}$$

____

3. Limestone samples are mainly calcium carbonate. When a 0.750 g limestone is dissolved in hydrochloric acid, 165 mL of carbon dioxide gas is evolved at STP. What is the percentage of calcium carbonate in the limestone? The equation for the reaction is

$$CaCO_{3(s)} + 2\ HCl_{(aq)} \longrightarrow CaCl_{2(aq)} + H_2O_{(l)} + CO_{2(g)}$$

4. What is the minimum STP volume of hydrogen sulfide gas required to precipitate 0.555 g of bismuth sulfide? The equation for the reaction is

$$2\ Bi(NO_3)_{3(aq)} + 3\ H_2S_{(g)} \longrightarrow Bi_2S_{3(s)} + 6\ HNO_{3(aq)}$$

5. (optional) The insecticide lindane, $C_6H_6Cl_6$, is prepared from benzene and chlorine gas in the presence of ultraviolet light. If 150 mL of chlorine gas at STP is reacted with 150 mg of benzene, C_6H_6, what is the mass of lindane produced? The equation for the reaction is

$$C_6H_{6(l)} + 3\ Cl_{2(g)} \xrightarrow{UV} C_6H_6Cl_{6(s)}$$

8

Ionic Equations

OBJECTIVES

1. To gain experience in observing the electrical conductivity of ionic and molecular substances.
2. To determine if a substance is a strong electrolyte, weak electrolyte, or nonelectrolyte.
3. To follow the course of a chemical reaction by observing electrical conductivity.
4. To become proficient in writing net ionic equations.

DISCUSSION

Electrical conductivity is based on the principle of electron movement from one point to another. Metals are good conductors of electricity because they allow for the flow of electrons. Rubber is a poor conductor because it does not allow electron movement. Pure water is considered to be a nonconductor. However, when a substance dissolves in water to form ions, the ions are capable of conducting an electric current. If the substance is highly ionized, the solution is a strong conductor. A slightly ionized solute is observed to be a weak conductor. When few, if any, ions are present, the substance is a nonconductor.

An ionic substance dissolves in water to form separate positive and negative ions. Since these opposite charges are electrostatically attracted, it is necessary to reduce the attraction in order for the positive and negative ions to separate. This electrostatic attraction is reduced by the polar water molecules which cluster about each ion. As the electrostatic attraction is reduced, the positive and negative ions separate naturally.

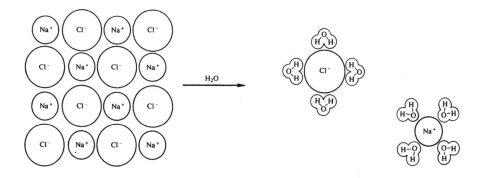

FIGURE 21-1 Dissociation of salt into sodium ions and chloride ions. Notice that the negative end of the polar water molecule is attracted to the positive sodium ion. The positive end of the water molecule is attracted to the negative chloride ion.

Solutions that can conduct an electric current are termed electrolytes and those that cannot are called nonelectrolytes. Electrolytes may be further divided into two groups, strong electrolytes and weak electrolytes. Table 21-1 lists common examples of the three types of electrolytes.

TABLE 21-1 STRONG AND WEAK
ELECTROLYTES AND NONELECTROLYTES

Strong Electrolytes	Weak Electrolytes	Nonelectrolytes
Most soluble salts	Insoluble salts	Sugar
Strong acids	Most acids	Alcohol
(HCl, HNO$_3$,	Most bases	Water
H$_2$SO$_4$, HClO$_4$)		
Strong bases		
(LiOH, NaOH, KOH,		
Ca(OH)$_2$, Sr(OH)$_2$,		
Ba(OH)$_2$)		

In this experiment you will be testing conductivity using an apparatus that has two wires serving as electrodes (Figure 21-2). If the electrodes are immersed in a strongly conducting solution, the circuit is completed and the light bulb in the apparatus glows brightly. A weak electrolyte has few ions in solution and produces only a dull glow in the bulb. A nonelectrolyte does not conduct current and hence the bulb does not glow.

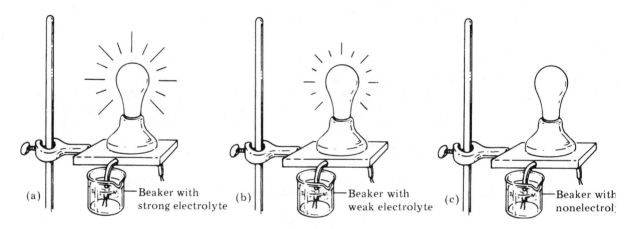

(a) —Beaker with strong electrolyte   (b) —Beaker with weak electrolyte   (c) —Beaker with nonelectrol

FIGURE 21-2   Conductivity apparatus testing (a) a strong electrolyte, (b) a weak electrolyte, and (c) a nonelectrolyte.

Since strong electrolytes are highly ionized, we should indicate the substance in solution as individual ions.

EXAMPLE 21-1   Strong Electrolyte

Aluminum chloride solution is observed to produce a bright glow from the bulb in the conductivity apparatus. Write AlCl$_3$ as it exists in solution.

Solution: Strong conductivity indicates mostly ions in solution, thus, Al^{3+}$_{(aq)}$ + 3Cl^{1-}$_{(aq)}$.

Conversely, weak electrolytes and nonelectrolytes produce few ions in solution and therefore exist primarily in the molecular form.

EXAMPLE 21-2   Weak Electrolyte

Sulfurous acid is observed to produce a dull glow from the bulb in the conductivity apparatus. Portray H_2SO_3 in aqueous solution.

Solution: Weak conductivity indicates mostly undissociated molecules in solution; thus, $H_2SO_{3\,(aq)}$.

Example 21-3   Nonelectrolyte

A glucose solution is observed to give no glow from the bulb in the conductivity apparatus. Write $C_6H_{12}O_6$ as it exists in solution.

Solution: No conductivity indicates glucose is molecular in solution; thus, $C_6H_{12}O_{6\,(aq)}$.

Writing Net Ionic Equations

Given the molecular equation for a reaction, balance it by inspection. Change the *molecular equation* into an *ionic equation* using the following guidelines.

1. Each formula of a compound in the molecular equation changes to the *ionic form* if it is a strong electrolyte. Examples include soluble salts, a few acids, and most group IA and IIA hydroxides (bases). The following illustrates changing a formula into ions:

    H_2SO_4 is written $2H^{1+} + SO_4^{2-}$ and $3Ca(NO_3)_2$ is written $3Ca^{2+} + 6NO_3^{1-}$.

2. Each formula of a compound in the molecular equation remains in the *molecular form* if it is a weak electrolyte or nonelectrolyte. Examples include insoluble salts, weak acids and bases, and water.
3. Write the net ionic equation by eliminating those ions not having undergone any change (spectator ions). *Spectator ions are identical* on both sides of the equation. Check the equation for balance.

EXAMPLE 21-4

$$H_2SO_{4\,(aq)} + 2\,NaOH_{(aq)} \longrightarrow Na_2SO_{4\,(aq)} + 2\,H_2O_{(\ell)}$$

$$2\,H^{1+}{}_{(aq)} + \cancel{SO_4}^{2-}{}_{(aq)} + 2\,\cancel{Na}^{1+}{}_{(aq)} + 2\,OH^{1-}{}_{(aq)} \longrightarrow 2\,\cancel{Na}^{1+}{}_{(aq)} + \cancel{SO_4}^{2-}{}_{(aq)} + 2\,H_2O_{(\ell)}$$

$$H^{1+}{}_{(aq)} + OH^{1-}{}_{(aq)} \longrightarrow H_2O_{(\ell)}$$

EXAMPLE 21-5

$$CaCl_{2\,(aq)} + K_2CO_{3\,(aq)} \longrightarrow CaCO_{3\,(s)} + 2\,KCl_{(aq)}$$

$$Ca^{2+}{}_{(aq)} + 2\,\cancel{Cl}^{1-}{}_{(aq)} + 2\,\cancel{K}^{1+}{}_{(aq)} + CO_3{}^{2-}{}_{(aq)} \longrightarrow CaCO_{3\,(s)} + 2\,\cancel{K}^{1+}{}_{(aq)} + 2\,\cancel{Cl}^{1-}{}_{(aq)}$$

$$Ca^{2+}{}_{(aq)} + CO_3{}^{2-}{}_{(aq)} \longrightarrow CaCO_{3\,(s)}$$

EXAMPLE 21-6

$$HCl_{(aq)} + NaC_2H_3O_{2\,(aq)} \longrightarrow NaCl_{(aq)} + HC_2H_3O_{2\,(aq)}$$

$$H^{1+}{}_{(aq)} + \cancel{Cl}^{1-}{}_{(aq)} + \cancel{Na}^{1+}{}_{(aq)} + C_2H_3O_2{}^{1-}{}_{(aq)} \longrightarrow \cancel{Na}^{1+}{}_{(aq)} + \cancel{Cl}^{1-}{}_{(aq)} + HC_2H_3O_{2\,(aq)}$$

$$H^{1+}{}_{(aq)} + C_2H_3O_2{}^{1-}{}_{(aq)} \longrightarrow HC_2H_3O_{2\,(aq)}$$

EXAMPLE 21-7

$$2\,H_3PO_{4\,(aq)} + 3\,Ba(OH)_{2\,(aq)} \longrightarrow Ba_3(PO_4)_{2\,(s)} + 6\,H_2O_{(\ell)}$$

$$2\,H_3PO_{4\,(aq)} + 3\,Ba^{2+}{}_{(aq)} + 6\,OH^{1-}{}_{(aq)} \longrightarrow Ba_3(PO_4)_{2\,(s)} + 6\,H_2O_{(\ell)}$$

No spectator ions: net ionic and total ionic equations are the same.

EXAMPLE 21-8

$$2\,Al(NO_3)_{3\,(aq)} + 3\,MgCl_{2\,(aq)} \longrightarrow 2\,AlCl_{3\,(aq)} + 3\,Mg(NO_3)_{2\,(aq)}$$

$$2\,\cancel{Al^{3+}}{}_{(aq)} + 6\,\cancel{NO_3^{1-}}{}_{(aq)} + 3\,\cancel{Mg^{2+}}{}_{(aq)} + 6\,\cancel{Cl^{1-}}{}_{(aq)} \longrightarrow$$
$$2\,\cancel{Al^{3+}}{}_{(aq)} + 6\,\cancel{Cl^{1-}}{}_{(aq)} + 3\,\cancel{Mg^{2+}}{}_{(aq)} + 6\,\cancel{NO_3^{1-}}{}_{(aq)}$$

No reaction: spectator ions only.

EQUIPMENT AND MATERIALS

Equipment
- conductivity apparatus
- small, dry beakers (6)
- straw (or 20 cm length of firepolished glass tubing)

A. Chemicals
- glacial acetic acid, concentrated $HC_2H_3O_2$
- sodium chloride, solid NaCl
- sucrose, solid $C_{12}H_{22}O_{11}$
- aluminum nitrate, 0.1 M $Al(NO_3)_3$
- barium chloride, 0.1 M $BaCl_2$
- copper (II) sulfate, 0.1 M $CuSO_4$
- ethyl alcohol, 0.1 M C_2H_5OH

- hydrochloric acid, 0.1 M HCl
- carbonic acid, 0.1 M H_2CO_3
- magnesium hydroxide, saturated $Mg(OH)_2$
- nitric acid, 0.1 M HNO_3
- potassium chromate, 0.1 M K_2CrO_4
- potassium hydroxide, 0.1 M KOH
- sodium hydroxide, 0.1 M NaOH
- sulfuric acid, 0.1 M H_2SO_4

B. Chemicals
- acetic acid, 0.1 M $HC_2H_3O_2$
- ammonia water, 0.1 M $NH_3 \cdot H_2O$
- potassium nitrate, 0.1 M KNO_3
- sodium carbonate, 0.1 M Na_2CO_3
- barium hydroxide, 0.1 M $Ba(OH)_2$

PROCEDURE

A. Conductivity Testing—Evidence of Ions

1. Test first the conductivity of distilled water and then tap water.

   NOTE: After the conductivity test of each chemical, rinse the electrodes with distilled water. Record your observations in the Data Table. Conclude whether the observations indicate a strong electrolyte, weak electrolyte, or non-electrolyte. Write the chemical species in either ionic or molecular form.

2. Pour about 10 mL of concentrated glacial acetic acid into a dry beaker and test the conductivity. Add several milliliters of distilled water *slowly* to the acid while continuously testing the conductivity.

3. Place a gram of solid sodium chloride in a *dry* beaker and test for conductivity. Add distilled water to the solid salt and retest the conductivity.

4. Put a gram of solid sucrose in a *dry* beaker and test for conductivity. Add distilled water to the solid sugar and retest the conductivity.

5. Test the conductivity of each of the following solutions:
   (a) aluminum nitrate, 0.1 M $Al(NO_3)_3$
   (b) barium chloride, 0.1 M $BaCl_2$
   (c) copper(II) sulfate, 0.1 M $CuSO_4$
   (d) ethyl alcohol, 0.1 M C_2H_5OH
   (e) hydrochloric acid, 0.1 M HCl
   (f) carbonic acid, 0.1 M H_2CO_3
   (g) magnesium hydroxide, saturated $Mg(OH)_2$
   (h) nitric acid, 0.1 M HNO_3
   (i) potassium chromate, 0.1 M K_2CrO_4
   (j) potassium hydroxide, 0.1 M KOH
   (k) sodium hydroxide, 0.1 M $NaOH$
   (l) sulfuric acid, 0.1 M H_2SO_4

B. Conductivity Testing—Evidence of Reaction

1. Test separately the conductivity of 10 mL of 0.1 M $HC_2H_3O_2$ and 10 mL of 0.1 M $NH_3 \cdot H_2O$. Pour the solutions together and retest the conductivity. Record your observations and conclusions; write balanced molecular, total ionic, and net ionic equations.
2. Add 1 mL of 0.1 M H_2SO_4 into a beaker containing 25 mL of water. Separately test the conductivity of H_2SO_4 and 0.1 M $Ba(OH)_2$. Continuously test the conductivity of the H_2SO_4 solution while adding 2 mL of $Ba(OH)_2$ dropwise. Record your observations and conclusions; write balanced molecular, total ionic, and net ionic equations.
3. Add 1 mL of 0.1 M $Ba(OH)_2$ into a beaker containing 25 mL of water. Test the conductivity. Allow the electrodes to remain in solution and blow through a straw into the solution until the conductivity is a minimum. Exhaling carbon dioxide into water produces carbonic acid, H_2CO_3. Record your observations and conclusions; write balanced molecular, total ionic, and net ionic equations.
4. Test separately the conductivity of 10 mL of 0.1 M Na_2CO_3 and 10 mL of 0.1 M KNO_3. Add the solutions together and retest the conductivity. Record your observations and conclusions; write balanced molecular, total ionic, and net ionic equations.

C. Net Ionic Equations—A Study Assignment

Balance the following molecular equations and write the total and net ionic equations. See the section, Writing Net Ionic Equations, for directions and examples.

1. $H_2SO_{4\,(aq)} + NH_3 \cdot H_2O_{(aq)} \longrightarrow (NH_4)_2SO_{4\,(aq)} + H_2O_{(\ell)}$
2. $FeCl_{3\,(aq)} + Mg(NO_3)_{2\,(aq)} \longrightarrow MgCl_{2\,(aq)} + Fe(NO_3)_{3\,(aq)}$
3. $Ba(C_2H_3O_2)_{2\,(aq)} + Na_2SO_{4\,(aq)} \longrightarrow BaSO_{4\,(s)} + NaC_2H_3O_{2\,(aq)}$
4. $K_2CO_{3(aq)} + HCl_{(aq)} \longrightarrow KCl_{(aq)} + H_2O_{(\ell)} + CO_{2\,(g)}$

PRELABORATORY ASSIGNMENT*

1. In your own words define the following terms: molecular equation, net ionic equation, nonelectrolyte, spectator ions, strong electrolyte, total ionic equation, weak electrolyte.
2. Explain the meaning of the symbols: (g), (ℓ), (s), (aq).
3. Give three examples for each of the following:
   - (a) strong electrolyte
   - (b) weak electrolyte
   - (c) nonelectrolyte
4. What will be observed when conductivity-testing a
   - (a) strong electrolyte?
   - (b) weak electrolyte?
   - (c) nonelectrolyte?
5. Write the following as they primarily exist in aqueous solution, that is, ionic form or molecular form.
   - (a) $KCl_{(aq)}$—a strong electrolyte
   - (b) $C_3H_5(OH)_{3(aq)}$—a nonelectrolyte
   - (c) $HNO_{2(aq)}$—a weak electrolyte
6. Why must the electrodes on the conductivity apparatus, as well as all beakers, be rinsed with *distilled* water?
7. What safety precautions should be observed in this experiment?

*Answers in Appendix II.

74

DATA TABLE FOR IONIC EQUATIONS

A. Conductivity Testing—Evidence of Ions

Substance	Observation	Conclusion	Ionic/Molecular
(Examples) { $LiOH_{(aq)}$	glows brightly	strong electrolyte	$Li^{1+}_{(aq)} + OH^{1-}_{(aq)}$
$HNO_{2(aq)}$	dull glow	weak electrolyte	$HNO_{2(aq)}$
$CH_3OH_{(aq)}$	does not glow	nonelectrolyte	$CH_3OH_{(aq)}$
1. $H_2O_{(\ell)}$—distilled			-Omit-
H_2O —tap			
2. $HC_2H_3O_{2(\ell)}$			
$HC_2H_3O_{2(aq)}$			
3. $NaCl_{(s)}$			
$NaCl_{(aq)}$			
4. $C_{12}H_{22}O_{11(s)}$			
$C_{12}H_{22}O_{11(aq)}$			

Substance	Observation	Conclusion	Ionic/Molecular
5. (a) $Al(NO_3)_3{}_{(aq)}$			
(b) $BaCl_2{}_{(aq)}$			
(c) $CuSO_4{}_{(aq)}$			
(d) $C_2H_5OH_{(aq)}$			
(e) $HCl_{(aq)}$			
(f) $H_2CO_3{}_{(aq)}$			
(g) $Mg(OH)_2{}_{(aq)}$			
(h) $HNO_3{}_{(aq)}$			
(i) $K_2CrO_4{}_{(aq)}$			
(j) $KOH_{(aq)}$			
(k) $NaOH_{(aq)}$			
(l) $H_2SO_4{}_{(aq)}$			

76

B. Conductivity Testing—Evidence of Reaction

Substance	Observation	Conclusion
1. $HC_2H_3O_2{}_{(aq)}$		
$NH_3 \cdot H_2O_{(aq)}$		
$HC_2H_3O_2 + NH_3 \cdot H_2O$		
molecular:	$HC_2H_3O_2{}_{(aq)} + NH_3 \cdot H_2O_{(aq)} \longrightarrow NH_4C_2H_3O_2{}_{(aq)} + H_2O_{(\ell)}$	
total ionic:		
net ionic:		
2. $H_2SO_4{}_{(aq)}$		
$Ba(OH)_2{}_{(aq)}$		
$H_2SO_4 + Ba(OH)_2$		
molecular:	$H_2SO_4{}_{(aq)} + Ba(OH)_2{}_{(aq)} \longrightarrow BaSO_4{}_{(s)} + H_2O_{(\ell)}$	
total ionic:		
net ionic:		
3. $Ba(OH)_2{}_{(aq)}$		
$Ba(OH)_2 + H_2CO_3$		
molecular:	$Ba(OH)_2{}_{(aq)} + H_2CO_3{}_{(aq)} \longrightarrow BaCO_3{}_{(s)} + H_2O_{(\ell)}$	
total ionic:		
net ionic:		
4. $Na_2CO_3{}_{(aq)}$		
$KNO_3{}_{(aq)}$		
$Na_2CO_3 + KNO_3$		
molecular:	$Na_2CO_3{}_{(aq)} + KNO_3{}_{(aq)} \longrightarrow K_2CO_3{}_{(aq)} + NaNO_3{}_{(aq)}$	
total ionic:		
net ionic:		

C. Net Ionic Equations—A Study Assignment

1. molecular: $H_2SO_{4(aq)} + NH_3 \cdot H_2O_{(aq)} \longrightarrow (NH_4)_2SO_{4(aq)} + H_2O_{(\ell)}$

   total ionic:

   net ionic:

2. molecular: $FeCl_{3(aq)} + Mg(NO_3)_{2(aq)} \longrightarrow MgCl_{2(aq)} + Fe(NO_3)_{3(aq)}$

   total ionic:

   net ionic:

3. molecular: $Ba(C_2H_3O_2)_{2(aq)} + Na_2SO_{4(aq)} \longrightarrow BaSO_{4(s)} + NaC_2H_3O_{2(aq)}$

   total ionic:

   net ionic:

4. molecular: $K_2CO_{3(aq)} + HCl_{(aq)} \longrightarrow KCl_{(aq)} + H_2O_{(\ell)} + CO_{2(g)}$

   total ionic:

   net ionic:

NAME _____

1. Explain why distilled water is a nonelectrolyte and tap water is a weak electrolyte. (Procedure A.1)

_____

2. Why does concentrated glacial acetic acid act first as a nonconductor and then behave as a weak conductor with the addition of water (another nonconductor)? (A.2)

_____

3. Why does solid sodium chloride act as a nonelectrolyte while the aqueous solution acts as a strong electrolyte? (A.3)

_____

4. Study the net ionic equation for $HC_2H_3O_2$ and $NH_3 \cdot H_2O$ and explain why the solutions are weak electrolytes individually but a strong conductor when mixed. (B. 1)

_____

5. Study the net ionic equation for H_2SO_4 and $Ba(OH)_2$ and explain why the solutions conduct individually but not together. (B.2)

_____

6. Barium hydroxide, $Ba(OH)_2$, acts as a strong electrolyte. Passing carbon dioxide gas through the solution reduces the conductivity to that of a nonelectrolyte. Explain this observation; refer to the net ionic equation. (B.3)

_____

7. Does the net ionic equation in Procedure B.4 agree with the criteria for chemical reaction, that is, precipitate, gas, etc?

_____

8. State whether each of the following is a: strong electrolyte (75 to 100% ionized), weak electrolyte (1 to 5 % ionized), or nonelectrolyte (0 to 1% ionized).

   (a) $CuS_{(s)}$

   (b) $Sr(OH)_{2 (aq)}$

   (c) $C_3H_7OH_{(\ell)}$

   (d) $NaHCO_{3 (aq)}$

9. Balance the molecular equations below and then write the total ionic and net ionic equations. Designate the state of each species by (s), (ℓ), (g), or (aq).

   (a) $ZnCl_{2 (aq)} + Na_2CO_{3 (aq)} \longrightarrow ZnCO_{3(s)} + NaCl_{(aq)}$

       total ionic:

       net ionic:

   (b) $AlCl_{3 (aq)} + NH_3 \cdot H_2O_{(aq)} \longrightarrow Al(OH)_{3(s)} + NH_4Cl_{(aq)}$

       total ionic:

       net ionic:

   (c) $HC_2H_3O_{2 (aq)} + Ca(OH)_{2 (aq)} \longrightarrow Ca(C_2H_3O_2)_{2 (aq)} + H_2O_{(\ell)}$

       total ionic:

       net ionic:

10. (optional) Define the difference between the terms ionization and dissociation. Give an example of each.

Neutralization Titration

OBJECTIVES

1. To standardize a sodium hydroxide solution with potassium hydrogen phthalate.
2. To determine the molar and percent by mass concentration of acetic acid in an unknown vinegar solution.
3. To gain experience in applying solution stoichiometry rules to an acid-base titration.
4. To acquire proficiency in the laboratory techniques of pipeting, titrating, and using phenolphthalein indicator.

DISCUSSION

A *titration* measures the volume of solution delivered from a buret. In this experiment sodium hydroxide is titrated into a flask containing an acid. After a sufficient amount of base is added to neutralize the acid in the flask, we will stop the titration. This is termed the *endpoint* and is signaled by an *indicator* that changes color. The indicator used in this experiment is phenolphthalein. Phenolphthalein is colorless in acid and red-pink in base. Therefore, the acid solution containing the indicator will be colorless until a very slight excess of base is titrated. At the endpoint the phenolphthalein changes the color of the solution to red-pink. A single drop of base is sufficient to bring about the color change. Figure 20-1 illustrates the sequence of steps in the titration.

This experiment begins with the dilution of 6 M sodium hydroxide to a concentration of about 0.3 M. Since the dilution provides only an approximate concentration, it is necessary to *standardize* the solution. That is, we wish to determine the sodium hydroxide concentration to three significant digits. We will choose solid crystals of potassium hydrogen phthalate (100 percent purity) for our standard acid.

The formula for the acid is $KHC_8H_4O_4$ although it is usually abbreviated KHP. After dissolving the acid in water, the base is standardized according to the equation:

$$KHP_{(aq)} + NaOH_{(aq)} \longrightarrow KNaP_{(aq)} + H_2O_{(\ell)}$$

PROBLEM EXAMPLE 20-1

1.555 g of pure KHP (mm = 204 amu) are dissolved in water and the solution is titrated with 29.60 mL of sodium hydroxide to a phenolphthalein endpoint. Find the molarity of the sodium hydroxide solution.

Solution: Referring to the preceding equation for the reaction and applying the rules of stoichiometry,

$$1.555 \text{ g KHP} \times \frac{1 \text{ mole KHP}}{204 \text{ g KHP}} \times \frac{1 \text{ mole NaOH}}{1 \text{ mole KHP}} = 0.00762 \text{ mole NaOH}$$

The molarity of the NaOH is found by

$$\frac{0.00762 \text{ mole NaOH}}{29.60 \text{ mL solution}} \times \frac{1000 \text{ mL}}{1 \text{ L}} = \frac{0.257 \text{ mole NaOH}}{1 \text{ L solution}} = 0.257 \text{ M NaOH}$$

The concentration of the standardized NaOH is 0.257 M. This agrees reasonably with the approximate concentration of 0.3 M from dilution.

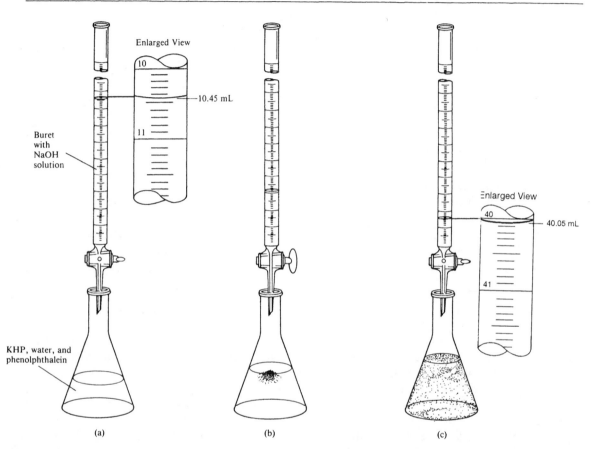

FIGURE 20-1 Titration of potassium hydrogen phthalate with sodium hydroxide solution. (a) Read the initial volume of base in the buret (10.45 mL). (b) Temporary flashes of pink indicate the endpoint is approaching. (c) A permanent pink color signals the base has neutralized the acid. Read the final volume of base in the buret (40.05 mL). The volume of NaOH required for the KHP sample is 40.05 mL − 10.45 mL = 29.60 mL.

After standardizing the sodium hydroxide solution, we will determine the acetic acid concentration in an unknown vinegar solution. A sample of vinegar will be titrated with the standard sodium hydroxide to a phenolphthalein endpoint. The equation for the reaction is

$$HC_2H_3O_{2(aq)} + NaOH_{(aq)} \longrightarrow NaC_2H_3O_{2(aq)} + H_2O_{(\ell)}$$

PROBLEM EXAMPLE 20-2

In the titration of a 10.0 mL vinegar sample, 35.05 mL of the above standard 0.257 M sodium hydroxide was required. Calculate the (a) molar and (b) percent by mass concentration of the acetic acid.

Solution:

(a) The moles of acetic acid titrated is

$$35.05 \text{ mL solution} \times \frac{1 \text{ L}}{1000 \text{ mL}} \times \frac{0.257 \text{ mole NaOH}}{1 \text{ L solution}} \times \frac{1 \text{ mole } HC_2H_3O_2}{1 \text{ mole NaOH}}$$

$$= 0.00901 \text{ mole } HC_2H_3O_2$$

and the molarity of $HC_2H_3O_2$ is

$$\frac{0.00901 \text{ mole } HC_2H_3O_2}{10.0 \text{ mL solution}} \times \frac{1000 \text{ mL}}{1 \text{ L}} = \frac{0.901 \text{ mole } HC_2H_3O_2}{1 \text{ L solution}} = 0.901 \text{ M}$$

(b) To calculate the percent by mass concentration, we must know the density of the vinegar solution, 1.01 g/mL, and the molecular mass of acetic acid, 60.0 amu.

$$\frac{0.901 \text{ mole } HC_2H_3O_2}{1 \text{ L solution}} \times \frac{60.0 \text{ g } HC_2H_3O_2}{1 \text{ mole } HC_2H_3O_2} \times \frac{1 \text{ L}}{1000 \text{ mL}} \times \frac{1 \text{ mL solution}}{1.01 \text{ g solution}} \times 100$$

$$= 5.35\% \ HC_2H_3O_2$$

EQUIPMENT AND CHEMICALS

Equipment

- graduated cylinder
- 1000 mL Florence flask
  with stopper to fit
- 125 mL Erlenmeyer flasks (3)
- funnel
- buret stand (or ring stand)
- buret clamp (or utility clamp)
- 50 mL buret
- 10 mL pipet
- pipet bulb
- 100 mL beaker
- wash bottle with distilled water

Chemicals

- dilute sodium hydroxide,
  6 M NaOH
- potassium hydrogen phthalate,
  solid $KHC_8H_4O_4$ (KHP)
- phenolphthalein indicator
- unknown vinegar solutions
  (4-6% $HC_2H_3O_2$)

PROCEDURE

A. Preparation of Standard Sodium Hydroxide Solution

1. Measure 25 mL of dilute sodium hydroxide (6 M NaOH) into a graduated cylinder and transfer to a 1000 mL Florence flask half filled with distilled water. Stopper the flask and swirl until homogeneous.

2. Condition a buret with the sodium hydroxide solution in the Florence flask. Place the buret in a clamp on a stand. Close the stopcock. Add sodium hydroxide solution into the buret through a small funnel.

   NOTE: Care should be taken not to overfill the buret.

3. Number three 125 mL Erlenmeyer flasks for identification. Record the mass of each flask. Accurately weigh out 1.2-1.8 g samples of KHP. Add about 25 mL of distilled water to each sample and heat as necessary to dissolve the acid crystals.

4. Prepare for the titration by following these steps.

   - *Clear the buret tip of bubbles.*
   - *Place one of the 125 mL flasks under the buret and position the tip as shown in Figure 20-1.*
   - *Observe the meniscus and record the initial buret reading.*
   - *Add two drops of phenolphthalein to each flask.*

   Titrate the KHP sample until a permanent red-pink endpoint is reached. Record the final buret reading.

5. Refill the buret, record the initial volume reading, and titrate the second KHP sample.
6. Repeat the titration for the third KHP sample.

   NOTE: SAVE THE SODIUM HYDROXIDE SOLUTION FOR PROCEDURE B.

7. Calculate the molarity of the sodium hydroxide solution for each trial. Record the average molarity in the Data Table of Procedure B.

B. Concentration of Acetic Acid in a Vinegar Solution

1. Obtain about 50 mL of unknown vinegar solution in a dry 100 mL beaker and record the unknown number.
2. Condition a pipet. Transfer a 10.0 mL sample of unknown solution into each of three 125 mL flasks.

   NOTE: It is not necessary to dry the flasks since they will not be weighed.

   Add 25 mL of distilled water and two drops of phenolphthalein into each flask.
3. Refill the buret and record the initial volume. Titrate the acetic acid in the first sample to a red-pink endpoint. Record the final buret reading.
4. Refill the buret, record the initial volume reading, and titrate the second vinegar sample.
5. Repeat the titration for the third sample.
6. Calculate the molarity of acetic acid in the unknown vinegar solution.
7. Convert the molar concentration to percent by mass. Assume a density of 1.01 g/mL for the unknown solution.

   NOTE: When the titrations are completed, rinse the buret with several portions of distilled water to remove all traces of the caustic sodium hydroxide solution.

1. In your own words define the following terms: conditioning, endpoint, indicator, molarity, percent by mass concentration, standardization, titration.
2. Which of the following is a serious source of experimental error?
    (a) The sodium hydroxide is not mixed thoroughly in the Florence flask.
    (b) The Florence flask is left unstoppered.
    (c) The buret is not conditioned.
    (d) The KHP samples are dissolved in 35 mL (not 25 mL) of distilled water.
    (e) Three (not two) drops of phenolphthalein indicator are used.
    (f) Bubbles are not cleared from the tip of the buret.
    (g) The Erlenmeyer flasks are not dried before weighing the KHP samples.
    (h) The Erlenmeyer flasks are not dried before pipetting the vinegar samples.
3. Observe and record the following buret readings.

(a) 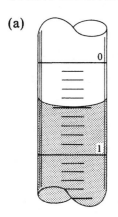   (b)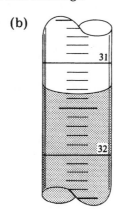

4. How can you tell when the endpoint is near? How much base is required at the end-point to flip the indicator from colorless to pink?
5. If the first KHP sample required 27.30 mL to reach an endpoint, what volume should be required for the second and third samples?
6. If the first 10.0 mL vinegar sample required 30.15 mL to reach an endpoint, what volume should be required for the second and third samples?
7. What safety precautions should be observed in this experiment?

NAME _____

SECTION _____

DATA TABLE FOR NEUTRALIZATION TITRATION

A. **Preparation of Standard Sodium Hydroxide Solution**

mass of Erlenmeyer flask + KHP	_____ g	_____ g	_____ g
mass of Erlenmeyer flask	_____ g	_____ g	_____ g
mass of KHP	_____ g	_____ g	_____ g
final buret reading	_____ mL	_____ mL	_____ mL
initial buret reading	_____ mL	_____ mL	_____ mL
volume NaOH	_____ mL	_____ mL	_____ mL

Show the calculation for the molarity of sodium hydroxide for trial 1.

Molarity of NaOH	_____ M	_____ M	_____ M
Average molarity of NaOH		_____ M	

B. **Concentration of Acetic Acid in a Vinegar Solution**   UNKNOWN # _____

Average molarity of NaOH (see Procedure A)			_____ M

volume $HC_2H_3O_2$ sample	_____ mL	_____ mL	_____ mL
final buret reading	_____ mL	_____ mL	_____ mL
initial buret reading	_____ mL	_____ mL	_____ mL
volume NaOH	_____ mL	_____ mL	_____ mL

Show the calculation for the molarity of acetic acid for sample 1.

Molarity of $HC_2H_3O_2$	_____ M	_____ M	_____ M

Show the calculation for the percent by mass concentration of acetic acid for sample 1.

Percent by mass concentration of $HC_2H_3O_2$	_____ %	_____ %	_____ %
Average percent by mass $HC_2H_3O_2$		_____ %	

POSTLABORATORY ASSIGNMENT NAME ____________________

1. A hydrochloric acid solution is standardized using 0.502 g of sodium carbonate. Find the molarity of the acid if 30.50 mL are required for the titration.

$$2\ HCl_{(aq)} + Na_2CO_{3(aq)} \longrightarrow 2\ NaCl_{(aq)} + H_2O_{(\ell)} + CO_{2(g)}$$

____

2. A 10.0 mL sample of household ammonia solution required 38.50 mL of 0.311 M HCl to achieve neutralization. Calculate (a) the molar concentration of the ammonia solution and (b) convert to percent by mass concentration of ammonia (17.0 amu), given a solution density of 0.983 g/mL.

$$HCl_{(aq)} + NH_3 \cdot H_2O_{(aq)} \longrightarrow NH_4Cl_{(aq)} + H_2O_{(\ell)}$$

(a) ____________________

(b) ____________________

3. If 19.65 mL of 0.145 M nitric acid is required to neutralize 50.0 mL of barium hydroxide solution, what is the molar concentration of the base?

$$2\ HNO_{3(aq)} + Ba(OH)_{2(aq)} \longrightarrow Ba(NO_3)_{2(aq)} + 2\ H_2O_{(\ell)}$$

____

4. A Rolaids tablet contains calcium carbonate to neutralize stomach acid. If 44.55 mL of 0.448 M hydrochloric acid is required to neutralize one tablet, how many milligrams of calcium carbonate are in a Rolaids tablet?

$$CaCO_{3(s)} + 2\ HCl_{(aq)} \longrightarrow CaCl_{2(aq)} + H_2O_{(\ell)} + CO_{2(g)}$$

5. (optional) A student carefully diluted 25.0 mL of 6 M NaOH solution in 475 mL of distilled water. Calculate the molarity of the diluted solution of base.

Explain why this diluted NaOH solution cannot be used as a standard solution of base.

Organic Model Exercise

OBJECTIVES

1. To build example model structures of the aliphatic hydrocarbons: alkanes, alkenes, alkynes.
2. To build example model structures of the aromatic hydrocarbons.
3. To build example model structures of the hydrocarbon derivatives: organic halides, alcohols, phenols, ethers, aldehydes, ketones, carboxylic acids, esters, amides, amines.
4. To identify the class of compound represented by the functional group in unknown model structures.
5. To acquire a three-dimensional perspective of organic compounds from the building of molecular models.

DISCUSSION

Organic chemistry is the study of compounds that contain the element carbon; compounds that do not contain carbon are termed inorganic. It is interesting to note that the element carbon is found in over two million different compounds. On the other hand, about 100,000 identified compounds do not contain carbon in their chemical formula. There are two reasons why over 90 percent of all compounds are organic. First, carbon is unusual in that it has the ability to self-link, forming chains of carbon atoms of varying length. Second, organic compounds typically contain several carbon atoms that may be joined together in more than one arrangement or configuration.

Compounds having the same molecular formula but a different configuration are termed *isomers*. For instance, the molecular formula C_4H_{10} may be constructed in two ways and still satisfy the bond requirements for carbon (four bonds) and hydrogen (one bond). Figure 23-1 illustrates the isomers of butane, C_4H_{10}.

Although the entire molecule as well as the individual bonds can be rotated in space to give what appear to be additional configurations for the formula C_4H_{10}, careful examination will reveal there are only two possibilities.

Although there are over two million organic compounds, they may be dealt with effectively by systematic classification. *Hydrocarbons* may be classified as alkanes, alkenes, alkynes, or aromatic. *Aromatic hydrocarbons* contain a benzene nucleus within the compound. If the hydrocarbon contains a *functional group*, such as an alcohol or ketone, it is considered a *hydrocarbon derivative*. Figure 23-2 illustrates an overall classification scheme.

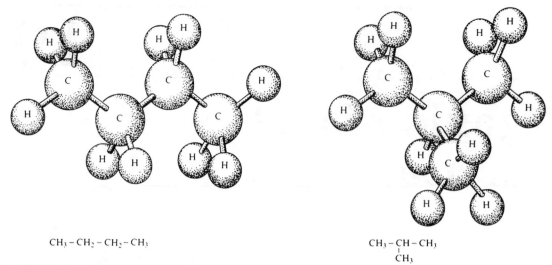

$$CH_3 - CH_2 - CH_2 - CH_3$$

$$CH_3 - CH - CH_3$$
$$CH_3$$

FIGURE 23-1   The two isomers of butane which share the molecular formula C_4H_{10}. The ball-and-stick model is shown above; the condensed structural formula below.

In this experiment we will build example molecular models for each of the hydrocarbons and derivatives shown in Figure 23-2. The following examples will serve to correlate the classes of compounds with the ball-and-stick models you will construct.

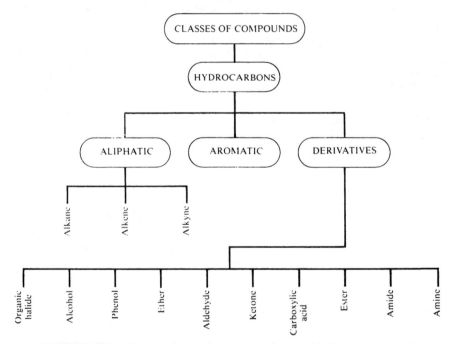

FIGURE 23-2   Classes of organic compounds organized into a systematic classification scheme.

Class of Compound	Example	Model Representation
alkane	$H_3C - CH_3$	
alkene	$H_2C = CH_2$	
alkyne	$HC \equiv CH$	
aromatic	C_6H_6	

Substituting a chlorine, bromine, or iodine atom for a hydrogen atom onto the hydrocarbon chain produces a class of compounds called the organic halides.

organic halide $CH_3 - Cl$

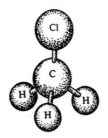

Many organic compounds, especially those of biological interest, contain oxygen as well as carbon and hydrogen. Oxygen has a bond requirement of two, and this may be satisfied in a number of ways. If one bond is attached to a carbon and the second bond to a hydrogen, an alcohol is formed. If both bonds are attached to carbon atoms, an ether is formed.

alcohol $CH_3CH_2 - OH$

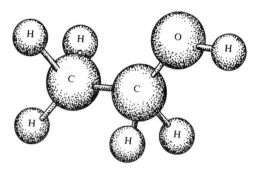

ether $CH_3 - O - CH_3$

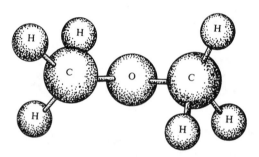

A phenol is simply a special example of an alcohol; that is, the —OH is attached directly to an aromatic group.

Oxygen can also satisfy its bond requirement of two by forming a double bond with carbon; this is termed a *carbonyl group*.

$$\begin{matrix} O \\ \| \\ - C - \end{matrix}$$

If the carbonyl group is at the end of the molecule—that is, one of the bonds is attached to a hydrogen—the functional group is an aldehyde. If the carbonyl is in the middle of the carbon chain—that is, both bonds are joined to other carbon atoms—the functional group is a ketone.

aldehyde $CH_3CH_2 - \overset{\displaystyle O}{\overset{\displaystyle \|}{C}} - H$

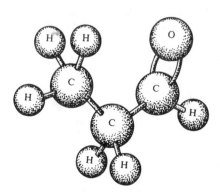

94

ketone

$$\text{CH}_3 - \overset{\displaystyle \overset{\text{O}}{\|}}{\text{C}} - \text{CH}_3$$

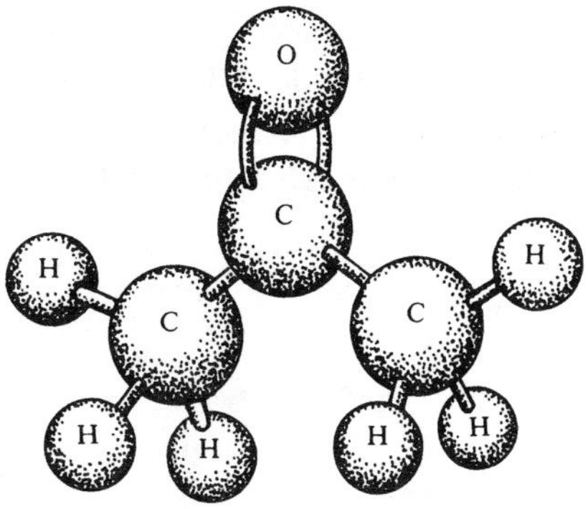

Another possibility is that the carbonyl may be attached to an —OH group. The resulting structure is found in the class of compounds called carboxylic acids.

carboxylic acid

$$\text{CH}_3 - \overset{\displaystyle \overset{\text{O}}{\|}}{\text{C}} - \text{OH}$$

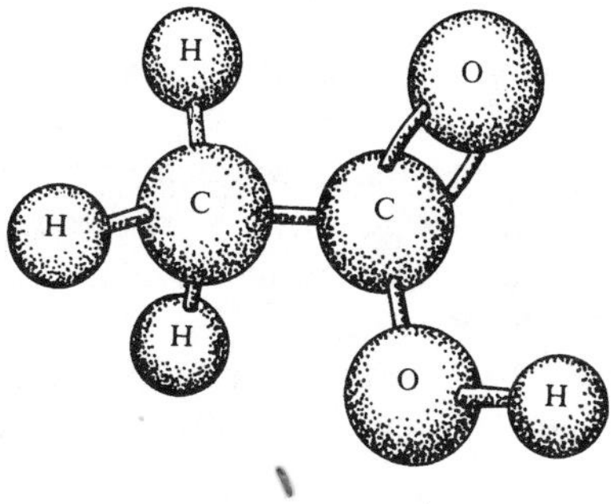

If we substitute a carbon for the hydrogen in the carboxylic acid group, this gives rise to the class of compounds called esters. Esters are noted for their typically fragrant odors.

ester

$$\text{H} - \overset{\displaystyle \overset{\text{O}}{\|}}{\text{C}} - \text{OCH}_3$$

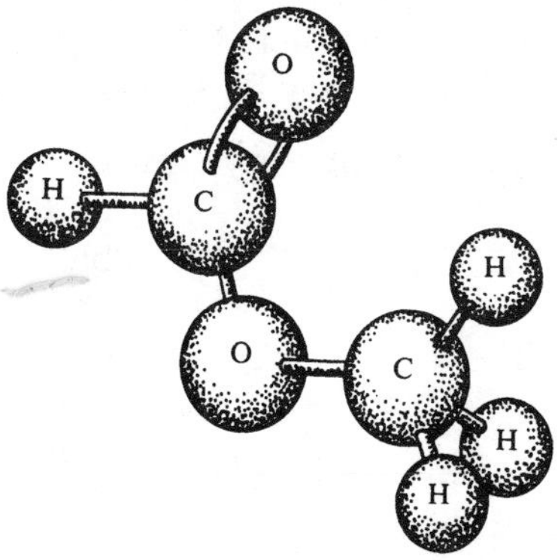

Starting with a carboxylic acid, let's remove the —OH and replace it with —NH_2. The resulting class of compound is called an amide.

amide

$$\text{H} - \overset{\displaystyle \overset{\text{O}}{\|}}{\text{C}} - \text{NH}_2$$

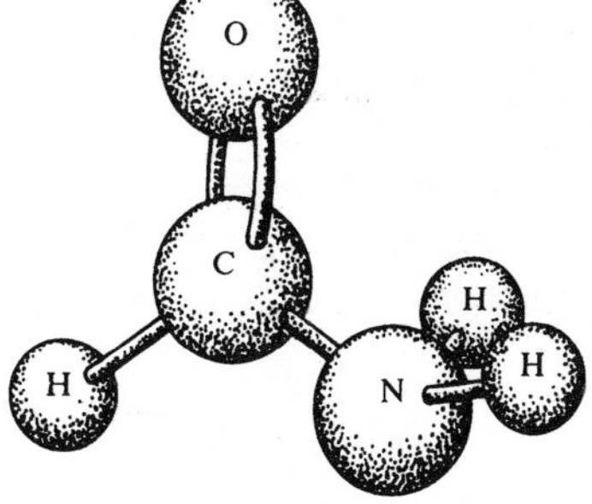

Finally, if we attach the —NH$_2$ group directly to a hydrocarbon, an amine results. Notice that the amine does not contain a carbonyl group.

amine   CH$_3$ — NH$_2$

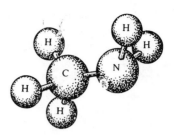

EQUIPMENT AND CHEMICALS

- molecular model kits

Directions for Using Molecular Models. When constructing a model, a hole in a ball represents a missing electron that is necessary in order to complete an octet. If two balls are joined together with a single connector, the connector represents a bond composed of two electrons. If two balls are joined together by two connectors, a double bond is indicated and represents four bonding electrons. Three connectors joining two balls represents a triple bond and a total of six electrons. The six electrons are perhaps more precisely referred to as three pairs of bonding electrons.

one connector — single bond (electron pair)
two connectors — double bond (two electron pairs)
three connectors — triple bond (three electron pairs)

As the model is constructed for a compound, all the holes in each ball should be filled with a connector. (Nitrogen may be an exception.) The color code for each ball is as follows:

white or yellow ball — hydrogen (one hole)
black ball — carbon (four holes)
red ball — oxygen (two holes)
blue ball — nitrogen (four or five holes)
green ball — chlorine (one hole)
orange ball — bromine (one hole)
purple ball — iodine (one hole)

PROCEDURE

A. Aliphatic Hydrocarbons

1. Construct the molecular models for the following *alkanes* and write their structural formulas in the Data Table:
   (a) methane, CH$_4$
   (b) ethane, C$_2$H$_6$
   (c) propane, C$_3$H$_8$
   (d) butane, C$_4$H$_{10}$
   (e) isobutane, C$_4$H$_{10}$

2. Construct models for the following *alkenes*:
   (a) ethylene, C_2H_4
   (b) propylene, C_3H_6
3. Construct the molecular model for the following *alkynes*:
   (a) acetylene, C_2H_2
   (b) methyl acetylene, C_3H_4

B. Aromatic Hydrocarbons   Construct the molecular models for the following *aromatic* compounds:

   (a) toluene, $C_6H_5CH_3$
   (b) para-xylene, $C_6H_4(CH_3)_2$

C. Derivatives of Hydrocarbons   Construct the molecular models for the following hydrocarbon derivatives:

1. *Organic Halides*
   (a) chloroform, $CHCl_3$
   (b) carbon tetrachloride, CCl_4
2. *Alcohols*
   (a) methyl alcohol, CH_3OH
   (b) ethyl alcohol, C_2H_5OH
   (c) propyl alcohol, C_3H_7OH
   (d) isopropyl alcohol, C_3H_7OH
3. *Phenols*
   (a) phenol, C_6H_5OH
   (b) ortho-cresol, $C_6H_4(CH_3)OH$
4. *Ethers*
   (a) dimethyl ether, CH_3OCH_3
   (b) diethyl ether, $C_2H_5OC_2H_5$
5. *Aldehydes*
   (a) formaldehyde, $HCHO$
   (b) acetaldehyde, CH_3CHO
6. *Ketones*
   (a) acetone, CH_3COCH_3
   (b) methyl ethyl ketone, $CH_3COC_2H_5$
7. *Carboxylic Acids*
   (a) formic acid, $HCOOH$
   (b) acetic acid, CH_3COOH
8. *Esters*
   (a) methyl formate, $HCOOCH_3$
   (b) ethyl acetate, $CH_3COOC_2H_5$
9. *Amides*
   (a) formamide, $HCONH_2$
   (b) acetamide, CH_3CONH_2
10. *Amines*
    (a) methyl amine, CH_3NH_2
    (b) ethyl amine, $C_2H_5NH_2$
    (c) propyl amine, $C_3H_7NH_2$
    (d) isopropyl amine, $C_3H_7NH_2$

D. Identification of Classes of Compounds   The instructor will provide numbered models of unknown organic compounds. Inspect each model, draw the structural formula in the Data Table, circle the functional group, and identify the class of compound to which it belongs. Each compound contains a single functional group. The following classes of compounds may be represented: *alkene, alkyne, organic halide, alcohol, phenol, ether, aldehyde, ketone, carboxylic acid, ester, amide, amine.*

PRELABORATORY ASSIGNMENT*

1. In your own words define the following terms: aromatic hydrocarbons, carbonyl group, functional group, hydrocarbon derivatives, saturated hydrocarbons, structural isomers, unsaturated hydrocarbons.
2. The following colored balls represent an atom of which element: black, red, white, green, orange, purple, blue?
3. What is used to construct a model representing two atoms of carbon joined by a single bond?
4. What is used to construct a model for a carbon atom and oxygen atom joined by a double bond?
5. Indicate the name of the class of compound for each of the following:

(a) $$-\overset{|}{\underset{|}{C}}-O-\overset{|}{\underset{|}{C}}-$$

(b) $$-\overset{|}{\underset{|}{C}}-Cl$$

(c) $$\overset{\backslash}{\underset{/}{C}}=\overset{/}{\underset{\backslash}{C}}$$

(d) $$-\overset{|}{\underset{|}{C}}-\overset{O}{\overset{||}{C}}-\overset{|}{\underset{|}{C}}-$$

(e) $$-\overset{O}{\overset{||}{C}}-OH$$

(f) $$-C\equiv C-$$

(g) $$-\overset{O}{\overset{||}{C}}-NH_2$$

(h) $$-\overset{|}{\underset{|}{C}}-OH$$

(i)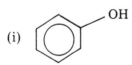

(j) $$-\overset{O}{\overset{||}{C}}-O-\overset{|}{\underset{|}{C}}-$$

(k) $-NH_2$

(l) $$-\overset{O}{\overset{||}{C}}-H$$

6. State the trivial name for each of the following alkyl groups:

(a) $CH_3 - \underset{|}{CH} - CH_3$

(b) $CH_3 - CH_2 - CH_2 -$

(c) $CH_3 -$

(d) $CH_3 - CH_2 -$

---

* Answers in Appendix II.

7. Draw and label the ortho(o), meta(m), and para(p) isomers of dichlorobenzene.

EXPERIMENT 23 NAME ______________________

DATE ____________ SECTION ______________________

DATA TABLE FOR ORGANIC MODEL EXERCISE

A. Aliphatic Hydrocarbons

1. *Alkanes*
   (a) methane, CH_4 (b) ethane, C_2H_6 (c) propane, C_3H_8

   (d) butane, C_4H_{10} (e) isobutane, C_4H_{10}

2. *Alkenes*
   (a) ethylene, C_2H_4 (b) propylene, C_3H_6

3. *Alkynes*
   (a) acetylene, C_2H_2 (b) methyl acetylene, C_3H_4

B. Aromatic Hydrocarbons

(a) toluene, $C_6H_5CH_3$ (b) para-xylene, $C_6H_4(CH_3)_2$

C. **Derivatives of Hydrocarbons**

1. *Organic Halides*
   (a)   chloroform, $CHCl_3$ (b)   carbon tetrachloride, CCl_4

2. *Alcohols*
   (a)   methyl alcohol, CH_3OH (b)   ethyl alcohol, C_2H_5OH

   (c)   propyl alcohol, C_3H_7OH (d)   isopropyl alcohol, C_3H_7OH

3. *Phenols*
   (a)   phenol, C_6H_5OH (b)   ortho-cresol, $C_6H_4(CH_3)OH$

4. *Ethers*
   (a)   dimethyl ether, CH_3OCH_3 (b)   diethyl ether, $C_2H_5OC_2H_5$

5. *Aldehydes*
   (a) formaldehyde, HCHO

   (b) acetaldehyde, CH_3CHO

6. *Ketones*
   (a) acetone, CH_3COCH_3

   (b) methyl ethyl ketone, $CH_3COC_2H_5$

7. *Carboxylic Acids*
   (a) formic acid, HCOOH

   (b) acetic acid, CH_3COOH

8. *Esters*
   (a) methyl formate, $HCOOCH_3$

   (b) ethyl acetate, $CH_3COOC_2H_5$

9. *Amides*
   (a) formamide, $HCONH_2$

   (b) acetamide, CH_3CONH_2

10. *Amines*
    (a) methyl amine, CH_3NH_2

    (b) ethyl amine, $C_2H_5NH_2$

    (c) propyl amine, $C_3H_7NH_2$

    (d) isopropyl amine, $C_3H_7NH_2$

D. Identification of Classes of Compounds

Model Number	Structure	Class of Compound
#1		
#2		
#3		
#4		
#5		
#6		
#7		
#8		
#9		
#10		

Answers to Prelaboratory Assignments

EXPERIMENT 1

1. See the Glossary, Appendix I.

2. See the diagrams of Common Laboratory Equipment, pages 4-5.

3. Directions for transferring chemicals are given in Appendices IX and X.

4. All chemicals have the potential to be dangerous, as you will see in the experiment.

5. Flush immediately with water and notify the instructor of any irritation.

EXPERIMENT 2

1. See the Glossary, Appendix I.

2. (a) 54.0 mL, 82.5 mL; (b) 5.40 cm, 4.15 cm

3. 0.790 g/mL

4. 2.4 g/mL

5. 3.25 g/cm^3

6. 0.00106 cm or 1.06×10^{-3} cm

7. • Be careful when using the pipet. See Appendix VIII
   • The instructor may wish to point out the disposal of methylene chloride and hexane in a special organic chemical waste container.

EXPERIMENT 3

1. See the Glossary, Appendix I.

2. Li, Na, and K; Ca, Sr, and Ba; Cl, Br, and I.

3. The wire must be clean. Sodium contamination is everpresent and must be distinguished from a positive test for a sodium compound.

4. The less dense hexane is immiscible with water and forms the upper layer. It is this upper layer that confirms the halide test.

5. • Wear eye protection when flame testing to avoid spattering.
   • Handle acids carefully and avoid breathing the vapors of concentrated hydrochloric acid.
   • Halide test solutions should be emptied into a designated organic waste container.

EXPERIMENT 4

1. See the Glossary, Appendix I.

2. 100.0 g

3. 1.00 cal/g $\times$ $^{\circ}$C

4. Two, because the temperature difference has two digits; e.g., 3.5°C.

5. Heat gain water = 800 cal = heat loss metal
    Specific heat Al = 0.202 cal/g $\times$ $^{\circ}$C

6. • Heat loss from the calorimeter to the surroundings (that is, from the styrofoam cup to the air).
    • Reading the thermometer to 0.1°C.

7. • Handle the laboratory burner and the elevated beaker of boiling water with caution.
    • Carefully transfer the hot metal into the calorimeter water to avoid splashing.

EXPERIMENT 5

1. See the Glossary, Appendix I.

2. Heat catalyst, no reaction, solid or precipitate, liquid, gas, aqueous solution.

3. • A gas is produced.
    • A precipitate is formed.
    • A color change is observed.
    • A temperature change is noted.

4. 2 mL

5. Colorless; pink

6. • Ignited magnesium ribbon produces intense heat.
    • Heating a mixture of powdered zinc and sulfur gives a highly exothermic reaction.
    • Avoid the fumes from hydrochloric acid.

7. 78.8 g/mole

EXPERIMENT 6

1. See the Glossary, Appendix I.

2. The crucible tongs eliminate weighing errors owing to fingerprints. The crucible should be cool before weighing so a hot crucible is not a problem.

3. The suggested periods for heating and cooling are intended as general guidelines. More important is consistency in the time intervals.

4. Heating magnesium in air produces both magnesium nitride and magnesium oxide. Water reacts with magnesium nitride producing ammonia gas and magnesium hydroxide. Reheating the crucible converts magnesium hydroxide to magnesium oxide.

5. If the magnesium has not completely reacted, small sparks will be observed when the crucible cover is lifted.

6. The reaction of the copper and sulfur is complete when no sulfur is left in the crucible. If in doubt, you can bring the crucible to constant weight.

7. • A hot crucible creates a buoyancy effect on the balance and mass readings are low.
    • The magnesium must not smoke excessively nor spark when the crucible cover is lifted.
    • The sulfur has a tendency to "creep" out of the crucible when heated. Any excess sulfur on the crucible must be heated and driven off as a gas.

EXPERIMENT 7

1. See the Glossary, Appendix I.

2. Particles of precipitate will be transferred prematurely into the filter paper and thus slow the filtration rate.

3.   To thoroughly remove the precipitate from the inside of the beaker.

4.   On occasion, particles of precipitate appear in the filtrate. This is due to either a small hole in the filter paper or overfilling the filter paper above the torn corner. At the discretion of the instructor, you may have to recycle the filtrate through a second weighed circle of filter paper. In that event, add together the masses of the two separate precipitates.

5.   • Incomplete precipitation (low results).
     • Coprecipitation of impurities (high results).
     • Precipitate in filtrate (low results).
     • Weighing filter paper with precipitate before it is completely dry (high results).

6.   Yes, co-precipitation or wet filter paper can give a percent yield above 100%.

7.   Transferring the precipitate from the beaker to funnel should be performed carefully to avoid breaking glassware.

EXPERIMENT 8

1.   See the Glossary, Appendix I.

2.   (g) indicates a gas; (ℓ) a pure liquid; (s) a solid substance; (aq) an aqueous solution.

3.   See Table 21-1.

4.   (a) Bulb glows brightly.
     (b) Bulb has a dull glow.
     (c) Bulb does not glow.

5.   (a) $K^{1+}_{(aq)} + Cl^{1-}_{(aq)}$;   (b) $C_3H_5OH_{(aq)}$;
     (c) $HNO_{2(aq)}$

6.   Any contamination of ions will give a strong conductivity test even for a weak electrolyte or nonelectrolyte.

7.   • Do not touch the exposed wire electrodes; a very serious shock can result.
     • Any chemicals contacting your skin or clothes should be washed immediately.

EXPERIMENT 9

1.   See the Glossary, Appendix I.

2.   (a), (b), (c), (f)

3.   (a) 0.50 mL;   (b) 31.35 mL

4.   Flashes of pink indicator persist longer. One drop, about 0.05 mL, will flip the indicator to permanent pink at the endpoint.

5.   The volume of base will vary depending upon the sample size of KHP.

6.   The volume of base should be consistent (30.15 mL) since the amount of vinegar is constant (10.0 mL).

7.   • Sodium hydroxide is caustic and could be severely harmful if a drop got in your eyes. On your skin, it creates a slippery sensation. In either event, wash immediately with water and notify the instructor.
     • Be especially careful not to overfill the buret by adding too much base into the funnel.
     • When inserting the pipet into the pipet bulb, hold your hands very close together to avoid snapping the pipet.
     • The pipet and buret are expensive pieces of glassware and should be handled with care.

EXPERIMENT 10

1.   See the Glossary, Appendix I.

2.   The element represented is carbon, oxygen, hydrogen, chlorine, bromine, iodine, and nitrogen, respectively.

3.   Two black balls and a single connector.

4.   A black ball and a red ball joined by two connectors.

5. (a) ether; (b) organic halide; (c) alkene; (d) ketone; (e) carboxylic acid;
    (f) alkyne; (g) amide; (h) alcohol; (i) phenol; (j) ester; (k) amine;
    (l) aldehyde

6. (a) isopropyl; (b) propyl; (c) methyl; (d) ethyl

7.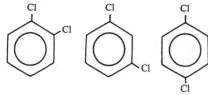

    ortho   meta   para

Using a Laboratory Burner

Although a variety of burners are found in chemistry laboratories, they all employ the same principle. Natural gas is allowed to flow into the barrel of the burner and mix with the air which contains oxygen. The ratio of gas to air can be adjusted, which in turn regulates the temperature of the flame. The more air that is available, the hotter the flame. Two typical burners are shown in Figure III-1.

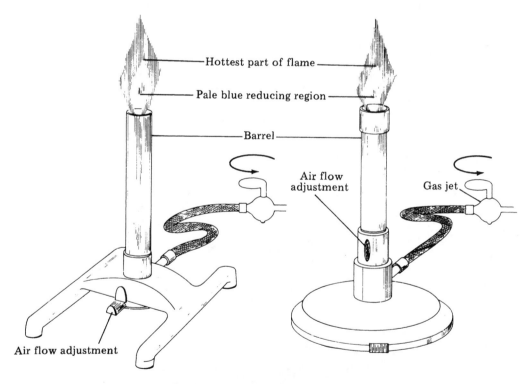

FIGURE III-1   Laboratory burners.

Steps in Operating a Burner

1. Close the air flow adjustment.
2. Open the gas jet.
3. Light the burner at the top of the barrel.
4. To obtain a hotter flame, open the air flow adjustment.
5. To shut off the burner, close the gas jet.

Using an Electronic Balance

An electronic balance is distinctly more sophisticated than the platform or centigram balance. This balance is an *expensive* electronic instrument that should be carefully used only after instruction in its operation. There are a variety of top-loading models available and most have milligram (0.001 g) precision (Figure VII-1).

Although it is not readily obvious, the principle of operation is similar to the less sophisticated beam balances. By rotating the weight adjustment knob, riders are substituted on and off the counterbalance beam which is inside the balance case and not visible. Some of the top-loading balances have an additional adjustment knob for a more precise reading of the milligram digit.

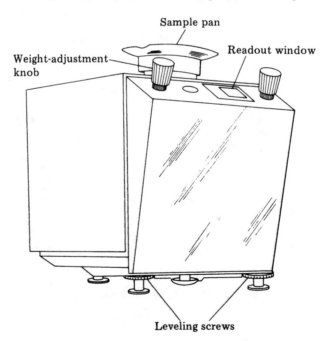

FIGURE VII-1   A top-loading electronic balance with milligram precision (0.001 g).

Using a Volumetric Pipet

In using a volumetric pipet, the following steps are useful to remember.

1. Lubricate the bulb before inserting the pipet. Hold your hands close together so as to avoid snapping the pipet, thereby avoiding a possible accident.
2. If the pipet is not dry, condition the pipet with a portion of the solution to be transferred. Dispose of the conditioning solution in the sink, unless otherwise directed.
3. Use the pipet bulb *(not your mouth)* to draw up the solution above the calibration line. Slip off the bulb and place your finger on the end of the pipet, thus preventing the solution from draining. Carefully allow the bottom of the meniscus to drop to the calibration line by moving your finger slightly.
4. Touch off the last drop of solution at the tip of the pipet and transfer the tip of the pipet into the receiving flask or beaker. Allow the solution to drain free into the receiving flask. Touch off the tip of the pipet. Do not blow out the last drop of solution, as the pipet is calibrated to deliver the specified amount (Figure VIII-1).

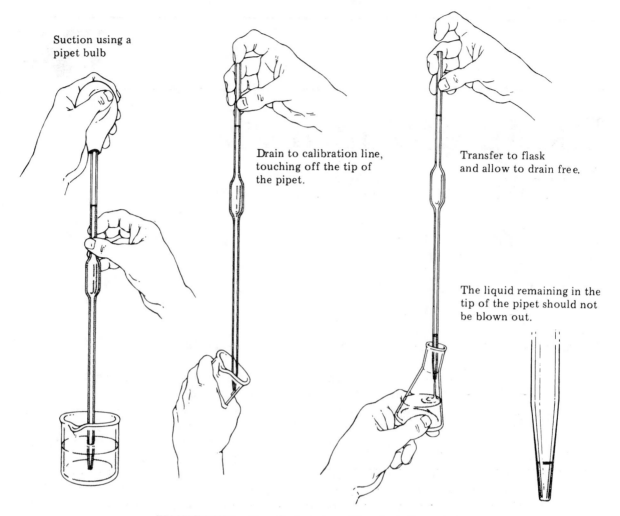

Suction using a
pipet bulb

Drain to calibration line,
touching off the tip of
the pipet.

Transfer to flask
and allow to drain free.

The liquid remaining in the
tip of the pipet should not
be blown out.

FIGURE VIII-1   Transferring a quantity of solution using a
volumetric pipet and bulb.

Transferring a Solid from a Reagent Bottle

Please observe the following general procedures.

1. Always obtain samples of crystals or powders at the shelf where the bottle is stored. Do not take the bottle to *your* laboratory station.

    NOTE: If an experiment calls for a *mass* of reagent, it is assumed a solid is being designated, as opposed to a liquid. A gram of substance is (very roughly) about a pea-sized portion.

2. Remove the glass stopper and scoop out a small portion of substance (Figure IX-1). Tap the scoopula with a pencil or your finger until the desired amount falls onto a watchglass, beaker, or other receiving vessel. Unless you are instructed otherwise, return the excess amount of substance on the scoopula to the reagent bottle.

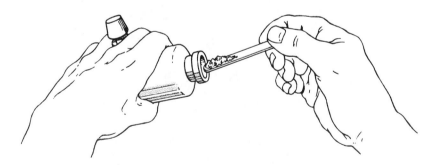

FIGURE IX-1   Scoop out a little of the material with a lab scoopula.

3. Place the same stopper back into the reagent bottle and return the bottle to its proper position on the shelf.
4. For larger amounts where a coarse measurement is tolerable, simply pour the solid into a beaker with a rolling motion from the reagent bottle.

Transferring a Liquid from a Reagent Bottle

Please observe the following general procedures.

1. Always obtain samples of liquids at the shelf where the bottle is stored. Do not take the bottle to *your* laboratory station.

    NOTE: If an experiment calls for a *volume* of reagent, it is assumed a liquid is being designated, rather than a solid. A standard 16 × 150 mm test tube contains about 20 mL. A standard dropper pipet delivers about 20 drops per milliliter.

2. Remove the glass stopper and hold the stopper between two fingers as shown in Figure X-1. Never set a stopper down. Pouring the liquid down the side of a glass rod minimizes splashing.

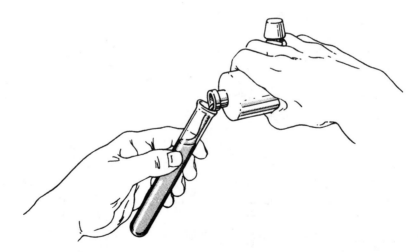

FIGURE X-1   Pouring a liquid directly from a reagent bottle.

3. Narrow glassware such as graduated cylinders and burets do not lend themselves to the use of a stirring rod. In such cases pour directly into the vessel (Figure X-1) or pour through a funnel.
4. Place the stopper back into the reagent bottle and return the bottle to its proper position on the reagent shelf.

Common Cations, Anions, and Polyatomic Ions

Cation	Name of Cation
Al^{3+}	Aluminum
Ba^{2+}	Barium
Bi^{3+}	Bismuth
Cd^{2+}	Cadmium
Ca^{2+}	Calcium
Cu^{1+}	Copper(I) or cuprous
Cu^{2+}	Copper(II) or cupric
Au^{3+}	Gold(III)
H^{1+}	Hydrogen
Fe^{2+}	Iron(II) or ferrous
Fe^{3+}	Iron(III) or ferric
Pb^{2+}	Lead(II) or plumbous
Pb^{4+}	Lead(IV) or plumbic
Li^{1+}	Lithium
Mg^{2+}	Magnesium
Hg_2^{2+}	Mercury(I) or mercurous
Hg^{2+}	Mercury(II) or mercuric
Ni^{2+}	Nickel(II)
K^{1+}	Potassium
Ag^{1+}	Silver
Na^{1+}	Sodium
Sr^{2+}	Strontium
Sn^{2+}	Tin(II) or stannous
Sn^{4+}	Tin(IV) or stannic
Zn^{2+}	Zinc

Anion	Name of Anion
Br^{1-}	Bromide
Cl^{1-}	Chloride
F^{1-}	Fluoride
H^{1-}	Hydride
I^{1-}	Iodide
N^{3-}	Nitride
O^{2-}	Oxide
P^{3-}	Phosphide
S^{2-}	Sulfide

Polyatomic Ion	Name of Polyatomic Ion
$C_2H_3O_2^{1-}$	Acetate
NH_4^{1+}	Ammonium
CO_3^{2-}	Carbonate
ClO_3^{1-}	Chlorate
ClO_2^{1-}	Chlorite
CrO_4^{2-}	Chromate
CN^{1-}	Cyanide
$Cr_2O_7^{2-}$	Dichromate
HCO_3^{1-}	Hydrogen carbonate or bicarbonate
HSO_4^{1-}	Hydrogen sulfate or bisulfate
HSO_3^{1-}	Hydrogen sulfite or bisulfite
OH^{1-}	Hydroxide
ClO^{1-}	Hypochlorite
NO_3^{1-}	Nitrate
NO_2^{1-}	Nitrite
$C_2O_4^{2-}$	Oxalate
ClO_4^{1-}	Perchlorate
MnO_4^{1-}	Permanganate
PO_4^{3-}	Phosphate
SO_4^{2-}	Sulfate
SO_3^{2-}	Sulfite

Generalizations of the Solubility of Solids in Water

1. Nearly all **nitrates** and **acetates** are *soluble*.
2. All **chlorides** are *soluble* except AgCl, Hg$_2$Cl$_2$ and PbCl$_2$. (PbCl$_2$ is soluble in hot water.)
3. All **sulfates** are *soluble* except BaSO$_4$, SrSO$_4$, and PbSO$_4$. (CaSO$_4$ and Ag$_2$SO$_4$ are only slightly soluble.)
4. Most of the **alkali metal** (Li, Na, K, etc.) salts and **ammonium** salts are *soluble*.
5. All **oxides** and **hydroxides** are *insoluble* except those of the alkali metals, and certain alkaline earth metals (Ca, Sr, Ba, Ra). [Ca (OH)$_2$ is only moderately soluble.]
6. All **sulfides** are *insoluble* except those of the alkali metals, alkaline earth metals, and ammonium sulfide.
7. All **phosphates** and **carbonates** are *insoluble* except those of the alkali metals and ammonium salts.

Electromotive Series

Li
K
Ba
Ca
Na
Mg
Al
Zn
Fe
Cd
Ni
Sn
Pb
(H)
Cu
Hg
Ag
Au

Concentrations of Dilute and Concentrated Acids and Bases

Reagent	Formula	Molar Concentration	Percent by Mass Concentration	Specific Gravity
acetic acid, conc	$HC_2H_3O_2$	17 M	99.5%	1.05
acetic acid, dil		6 M	34%	1.04
hydrochloric acid, conc	HCl	12 M	36%	1.18
hydrochloric acid, dil		6 M	20%	1.10
nitric acid, conc	HNO_3	16 M	72%	1.42
nitric acid, dil		6 M	32%	1.19
sulfuric acid, conc	H_2SO_4	18 M	96%	1.84
sulfuric acid, dil		3 M	25%	1.18
ammonia water, conc	$NH_3 \cdot H_2O$	15 M	58%	0.90
ammonia water, dil		6 M	23%	0.96
sodium hydroxide, dil	NaOH	6 M	20%	1.22

List of Elements with Their Symbols and Atomic Masses

Element	Symbol	Atomic Number	Atomic Mass[a] (amu)	Element	Symbol	Atomic Number	Atomic Mass[a] (amu)	Element	Symbol	Atomic Number	Atomic Mass[a] (amu)
Actinium	Ac	89	(227)	Helium	He	2	4.00260	Radon	Rn	86	(222)
Aluminum	Al	13	26.9815	Holmium	Ho	67	164.9303	Rhenium	Re	75	186.207
Americium	Am	95	(243)	Hydrogen	H	1	1.0080	Rhodium	Rh	45	102.9055
Antimony	Sb	51	121.75	Indium	In	49	114.82	Rubidium	Rb	37	85.4678
Argon	Ar	18	39.948	Iodine	I	53	126.9045	Ruthenium	Ru	44	101.07
Arsenic	As	33	74.9216	Iridium	Ir	77	192.22	Rutherfordium[b]	Rf	104	(261)
Astatine	At	85	(210)	Iron	Fe	26	55.847	Samarium	Sm	62	150.4
Barium	Ba	56	137.33	Krypton	Kr	36	83.80	Scandium	Sc	21	44.9559
Berkelium	Bk	97	(247)	Lanthanum	La	57	138.9055	Selenium	Se	34	78.96
Beryllium	Be	4	9.01218	Lawrencium	Lr	103	(257)	Silicon	Si	14	28.0855
Bismuth	Bi	83	208.9806	Lead	Pb	82	207.2	Silver	Ag	47	107.868
Boron	B	5	10.811	Lithium	Li	3	6.941	Sodium	Na	11	22.9898
Bromine	Br	35	79.904	Lutetium	Lu	71	174.967	Strontium	Sr	38	87.62
Cadmium	Cd	48	112.41	Magnesium	Mg	12	24.305	Sulfur	S	16	32.06
Calcium	Ca	20	40.08	Manganese	Mn	25	54.9380	Tantalum	Ta	73	180.9479
Californium	Cf	98	(251)	Mendelevium	Md	101	(256)	Technetium	Tc	43	98.9062
Carbon	C	6	12.01115	Mercury	Hg	80	200.59	Tellurium	Te	52	127.60
Cerium	Ce	58	140.12	Molybdenum	Mo	42	95.94	Terbium	Tb	65	158.9254
Cesium	Cs	55	132.9055	Neodymium	Nd	60	144.24	Thallium	Tl	81	204.37
Chlorine	Cl	17	35.453	Neon	Ne	10	20.179	Thorium	Th	90	232.0381
Chromium	Cr	24	51.996	Neptunium	Np	93	237.0482	Thulium	Tm	69	168.9342
Cobalt	Co	27	58.9332	Nickel	Ni	28	58.70	Tin	Sn	50	118.69
Copper	Cu	29	63.546	Niobium	Nb	41	92.9064	Titanium	Ti	22	47.90
Curium	Cm	96	(247)	Nitrogen	N	7	14.0067	Tungsten	W	74	183.85
Dysprosium	Dy	66	162.50	Nobelium	No	102	(255)	Unnilennium	Une	109	(266)
Einsteinium	Es	99	(254)	Osmium	Os	76	190.2	Unnilhexium	Unh	106	(263)
Erbium	Er	68	167.26	Oxygen	O	8	15.9994	Unniloctium	Uno	108	(265)
Europium	Eu	63	151.96	Palladium	Pd	46	106.4	Unnilseptium	Uns	107	(262)
Fermium	Fm	100	(257)	Phosphorus	P	15	30.9738	Uranium	U	92	238.029
Fluorine	F	9	18.998403	Platinum	Pt	78	195.09	Vanadium	V	23	50.9415
Francium	Fr	87	(223)	Plutonium	Pu	94	(244)	Xenon	Xe	54	131.30
Gadolinium	Gd	64	157.25	Polonium	Po	84	(209)	Ytterbium	Yb	70	173.04
Gallium	Ga	31	69.72	Potassium	K	19	39.0983	Yttrium	Y	39	88.9059
Germanium	Ge	32	72.59	Praseodymium	Pr	59	140.9077	Zinc	Zn	30	65.37
Gold	Au	79	196.9665	Promethium	Pm	61	(145)	Zirconium	Zr	40	91.22
Hafnium	Hf	72	178.49	Protactinium	Pa	91	231.0359				
Hahnium[b]	Ha	105	(262)	Radium	Ra	88	226.0254				

[a]Based on the assigned relative atomic mass of ^{12}C = exactly 12 amu; [b]name and symbol not officially approved; parentheses indicate the mass number of the isotope with the longest half-life.

Periodic Table of the Elements

GROUPS

PERIODS	1 IA	2 IIA	3 IIIB	4 IVB	5 VB	6 VIB	7 VIIB	8 VIII	9 VIII	10 VIII	11 IB	12 IIB	13 IIIA	14 IVA	15 VA	16 VIA	17 VIIA	18 VIIIA
1	1 008 **H** 1																	4 003 **He** 2
2	6 941 **Li** 3	9 012 **Be** 4											10 811 **B** 5	12 011 **C** 6	14 007 **N** 7	15 999 **O** 8	18 998 **F** 9	20 179 **Ne** 10
3	22 990 **Na** 11	24 305 **Mg** 12											26 982 **Al** 13	28 0855 **Si** 14	30 9738 **P** 15	32 06 **S** 16	35 453 **Cl** 17	39 948 **Ar** 18
4	39 0983 **K** 19	40 08 **Ca** 20	44 956 **Sc** 21	47 90 **Ti** 22	50 9415 **V** 23	51 996 **Cr** 24	54 938 **Mn** 25	55 847 **Fe** 26	58 933 **Co** 27	58 71 **Ni** 28	63 546 **Cu** 29	65 37 **Zn** 30	69 72 **Ga** 31	72 59 **Ge** 32	74 922 **As** 33	78 96 **Se** 34	79 904 **Br** 35	83 80 **Kr** 36
5	85 468 **Rb** 37	87 62 **Sr** 38	88 906 **Y** 39	91 22 **Zr** 40	92 9064 **Nb** 41	95 94 **Mo** 42	98 906 **Tc** 43	101 07 **Ru** 44	102 906 **Rh** 45	106 4 **Pd** 46	107 868 **Ag** 47	112 41 **Cd** 48	114 82 **In** 49	118 69 **Sn** 50	121 75 **Sb** 51	127 60 **Te** 52	126 904 **I** 53	131 30 **Xe** 54
6	132 906 **Cs** 55	137 33 **Ba** 56	138 906 *****La** 57	178 49 **Hf** 72	180 948 **Ta** 73	183 85 **W** 74	186 2 **Re** 75	190 2 **Os** 76	192 22 **Ir** 77	195 09 **Pt** 78	196 967 **Au** 79	200 59 **Hg** 80	204 37 **Tl** 81	207 2 **Pb** 82	208 981 **Bi** 83	(209) **Po** 84	(210) **At** 85	(222) **Rn** 86
7	(223) **Fr** 87	226 025 **Ra** 88	(227) ******Ac** 89	(261) **Rf** 104	(262) **Ha** 105	(263) **Unh** 106	(262) **Uns** 107	(265) **Uno** 108	(266) **Une** 109									

TRANSITION ELEMENTS

*Lanthanide series

140 12 **Ce** 58	140 908 **Pr** 59	144 24 **Nd** 60	(145) **Pm** 61	150 4 **Sm** 62	151 96 **Eu** 63	157 25 **Gd** 64	158 925 **Tb** 65	162 50 **Dy** 66	164 930 **Ho** 67	167 26 **Er** 68	168 934 **Tm** 69	173 04 **Yb** 70	174 967 **Lu** 71

**Actinide series

232 038 **Th** 90	231 031 **Pa** 91	238 029 **U** 92	237 048 **Np** 93	(244) **Pu** 94	(243) **Am** 95	(247) **Cm** 96	(247) **Bk** 97	(251) **Cf** 98	(254) **Es** 99	(257) **Fm** 100	(256) **Md** 101	(255) **No** 102	(257) **Lr** 103

Numbers below the symbol of the element indicate the atomic numbers. Atomic masses, above the symbol of the element, are based on the assigned relative atomic mass of ^{12}C = exactly 12; ( ) indicates the mass number of the isotope with the longest half-life.